KINDERGARTEN MATHEMATICS

ACTIVITY BOOK

Yeap Ban Har

Published by Marshall Cavendish Education
An imprint of Marshall Cavendish International (Singapore) Private Limited
Times Centre, 1 New Industrial Road, Singapore 536196
Customer Service Hotline: (65) 6411 0820
E-mail: tmesales@sg.marshallcavendish.com
Website: www.marshallcavendish.com/education

Marshall Cavendish Corporation
99 White Plains Road
Tarrytown, NY 10591
U.S.A.
Tel: (1-914) 332 8888
Fax: (1-914) 332 8882
E-mail: mcc@marshallcavendish.com
Website: www.marshallcavendish.com

First published 2008
Reprinted 2009, 2010, 2011 (twice)

Earlybird Kindergarten Mathematics (Standards Edition) Activity Book B
ISBN 978-0-7614-7018-2

Printed in Singapore by Times Printers, www.timesprinters.com

SingaporeMath.com Inc®
Distributed by
SingaporeMath.com Inc
404 Beavercreek Road #225
Oregon City, OR 97045
U.S.A.
Website: www.singaporemath.com

Earlybird Kindergarten Mathematics (Standards Edition) Activity Books can be used to supplement the Textbooks and complement the Big Books, or they may be used as a complete and fun activity-based program on their own.

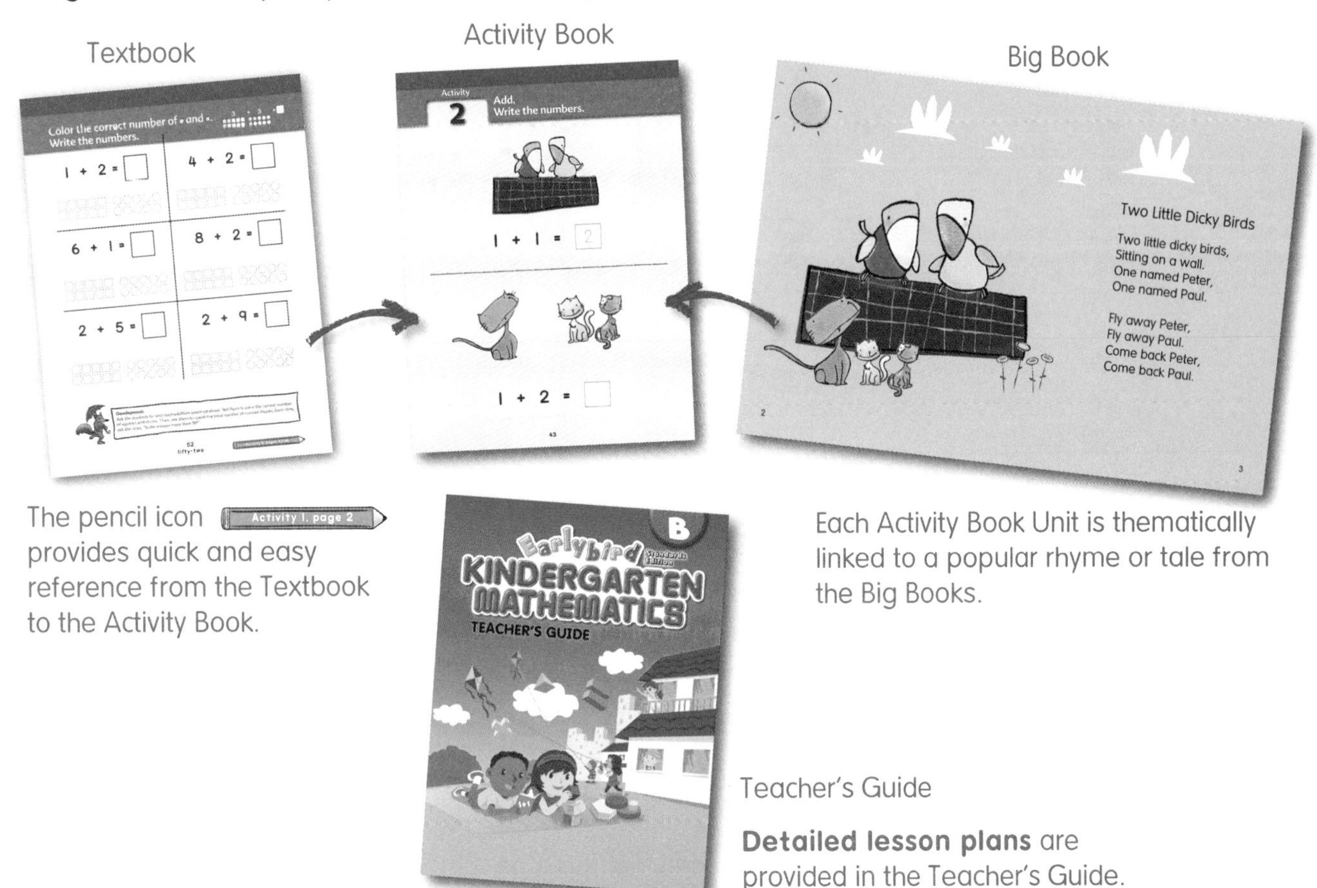

The pencil icon provides quick and easy reference from the Textbook to the Activity Book.

Each Activity Book Unit is thematically linked to a popular rhyme or tale from the Big Books.

Teacher's Guide

Detailed lesson plans are provided in the Teacher's Guide.

Earlybird Kindergarten Mathematics (Standards Edition) is designed to form the foundation level for the Primary Mathematics (Standards Edition) series. Mathematical concepts are systematically introduced and reinforced using the **Concrete → Pictorial → Abstract** approach.

Activities in the form of practical tasks provide hands-on experiential learning for students. This forms the basis of the **Concrete → Pictorial → Abstract** approach.

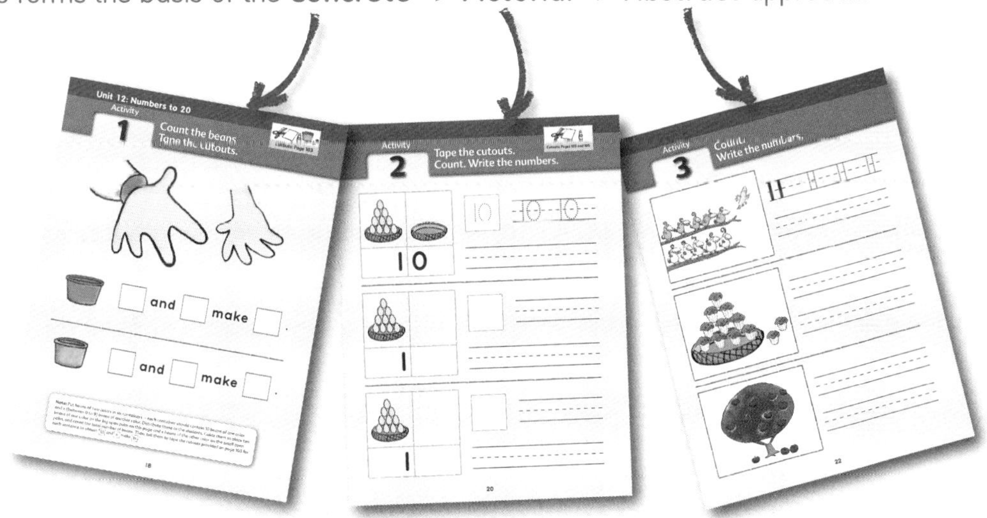

Students use cutouts provided in the book to work out math problems. Mathematical thinking skills are developed through concrete experience.

Some activities require the use of standard manipulatives and other materials. The materials and additional information required are indicated by the Toolbox and Notes.

Written exercises that focus on **repetition** ensure the reinforcement of mathematics facts and concepts.

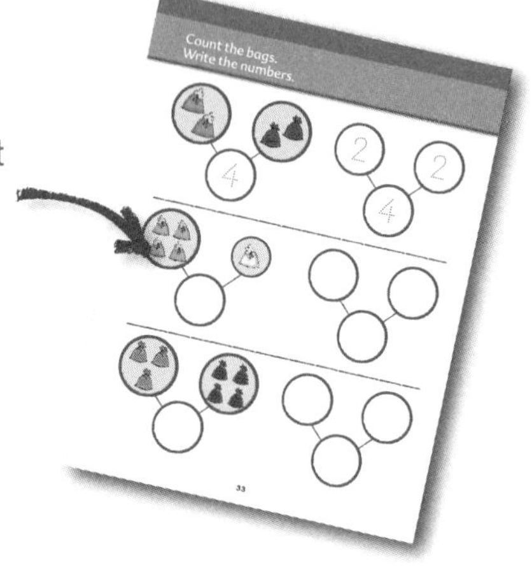

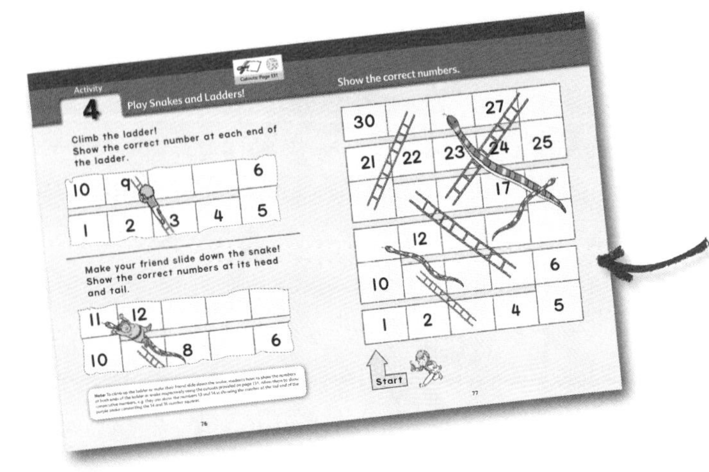

A **variety of activities** such as games and practical tasks help to engage students in the revision of mathematical concepts. The activities in each unit are carefully sequenced for **progression in level of difficulty**.

CONTENTS

Activity

1

Count.
Write the numbers.

7

3

3 is less than 7 .

Count.
Write the numbers.

☐ is more than ☐ .

Count.
Write the numbers.

☐ is less than ☐ .

☐ is more than ☐ .

Activity 2

Which has more? Circle the picture. Write the numbers.

There are more  .

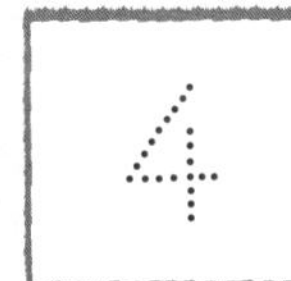

is more than

.

There are more  .

 is more than  .

Count.
Write the numbers.

7 3

7 is more than 3 .

4 more

Count.
Write the numbers.

☐ is more than ☐ .

☐ more

Activity

3

Which group has more? Check (✔) the box.

✔

Which group has more? Check (✔) the box. Write the number.

more

Which group has more? Check (✓) the box. Write the number.

Which group has fewer? Check (✓) the box.

Which group has fewer? Check (✓) the box. Write the numbers.

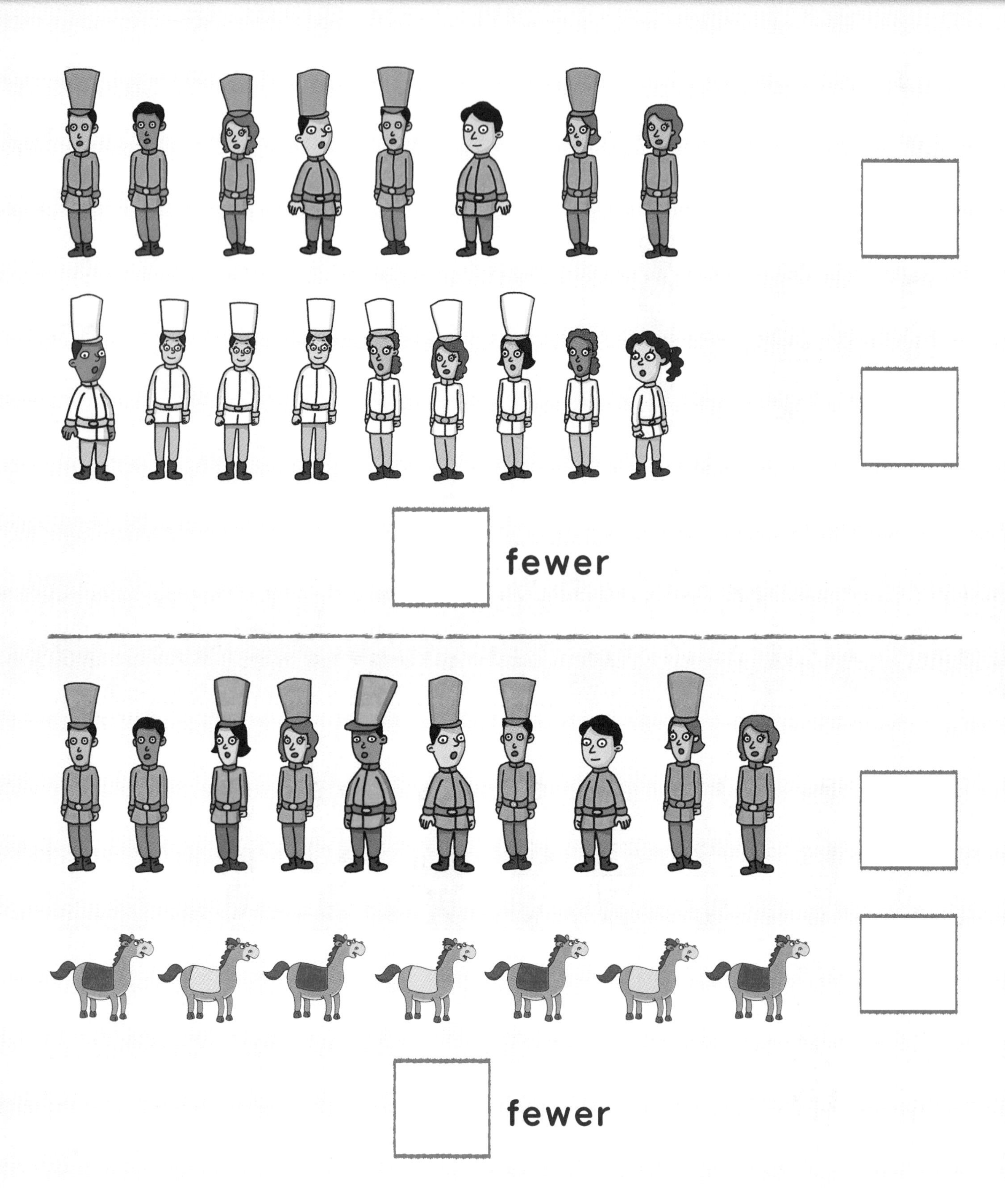

Activity

4 More or fewer? Circle the word.

There are

more / fewer

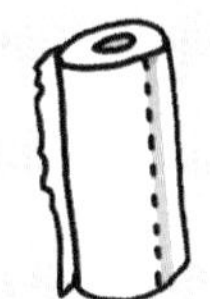 than 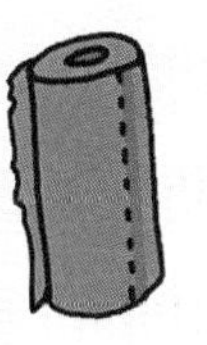 .

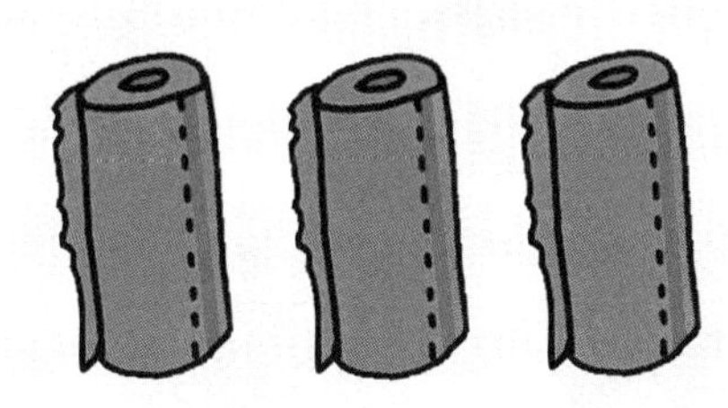

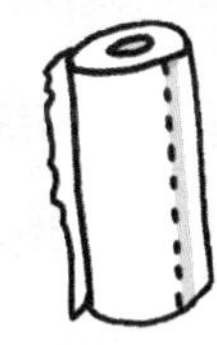

There are

more / fewer

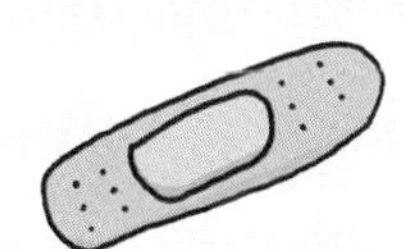 than  .

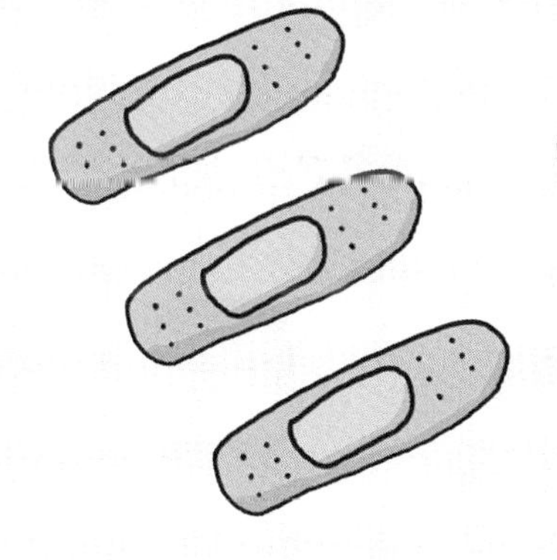

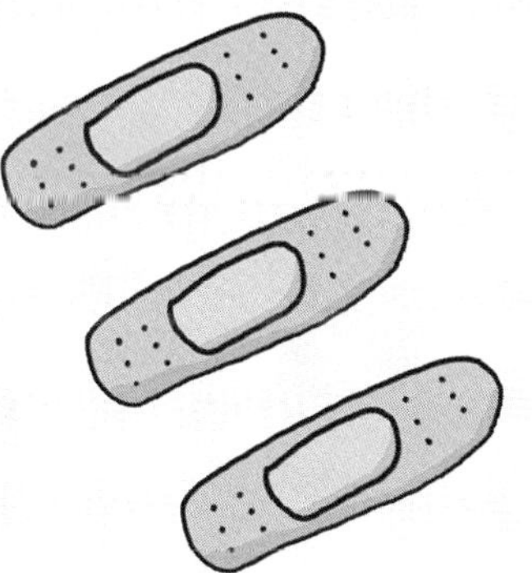

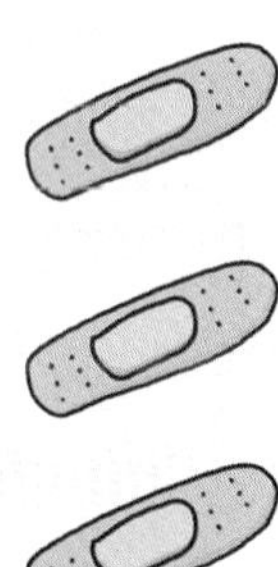

More or fewer?
Circle the words. Write the numbers.

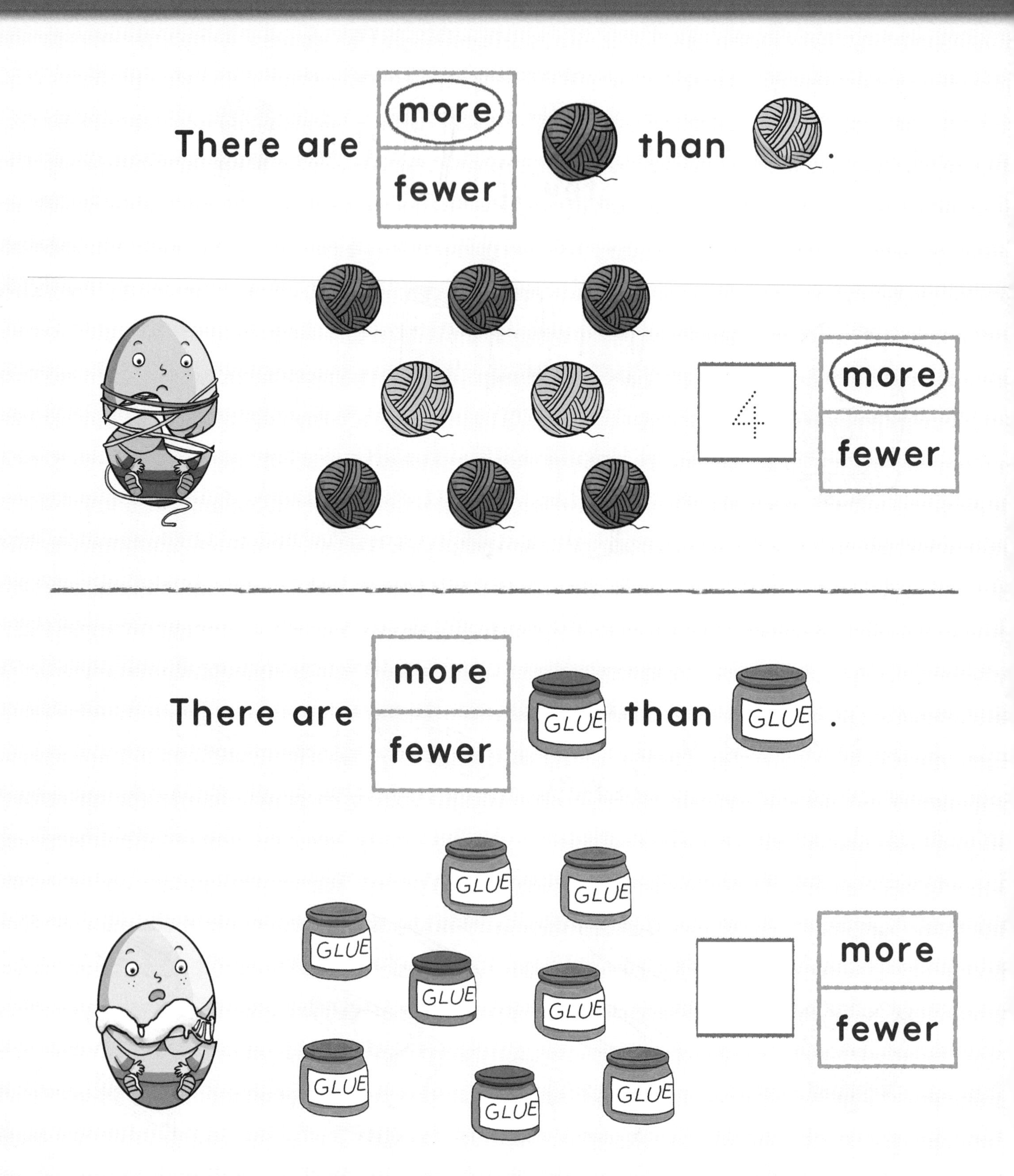

More or fewer?
Circle the words. Write the numbers.

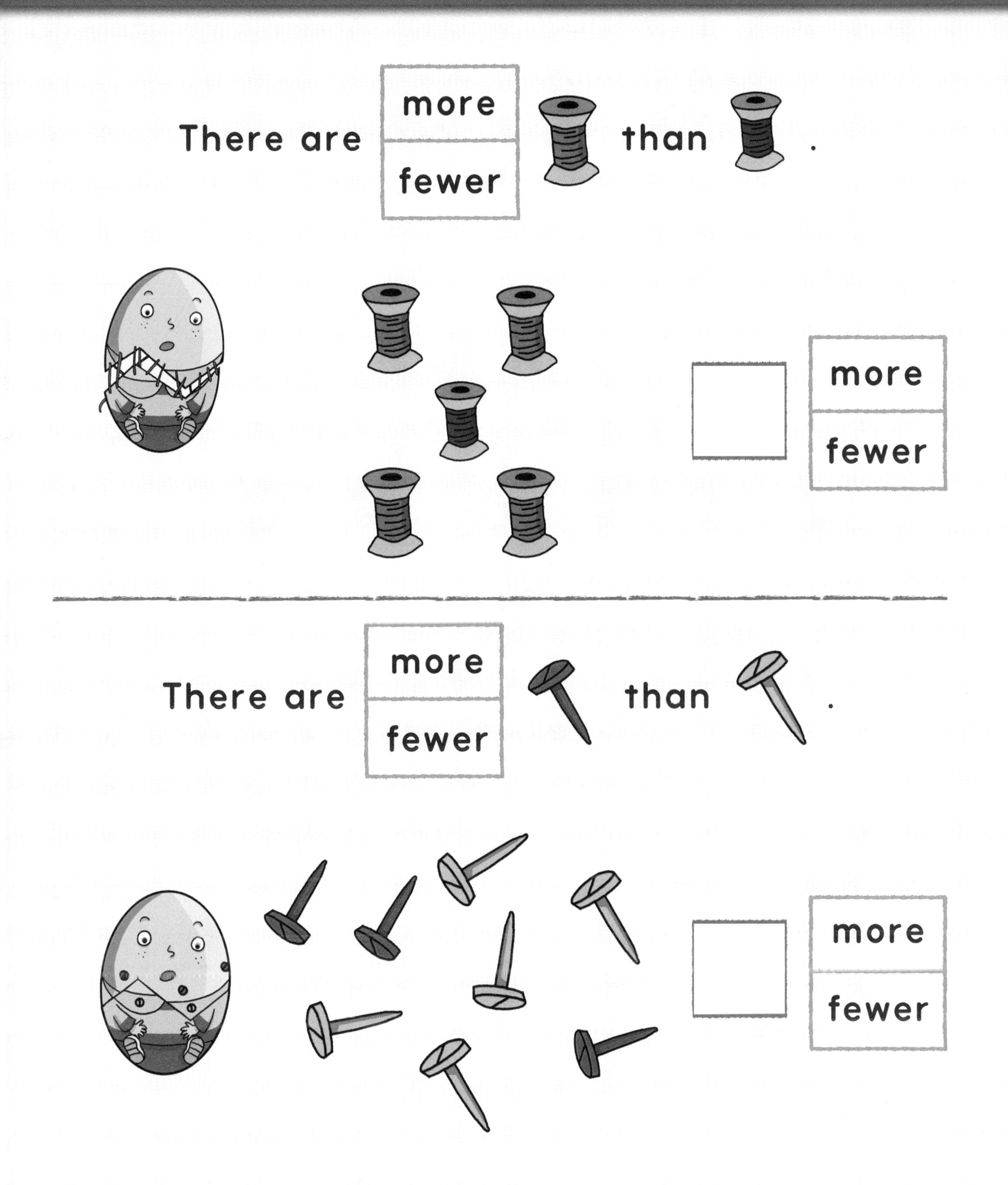

Activity

Count.
Write the numbers.

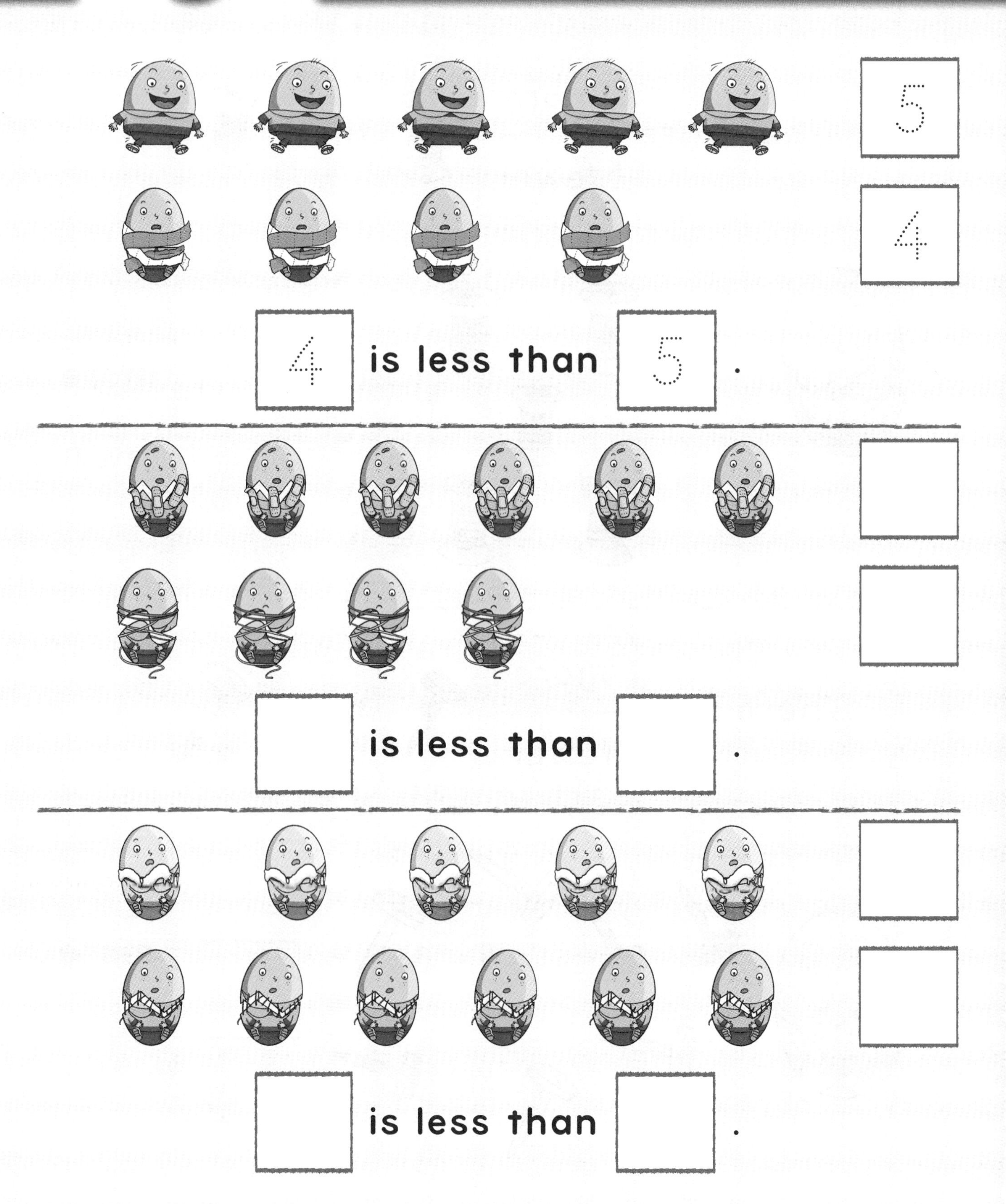

Count.
Write the numbers.

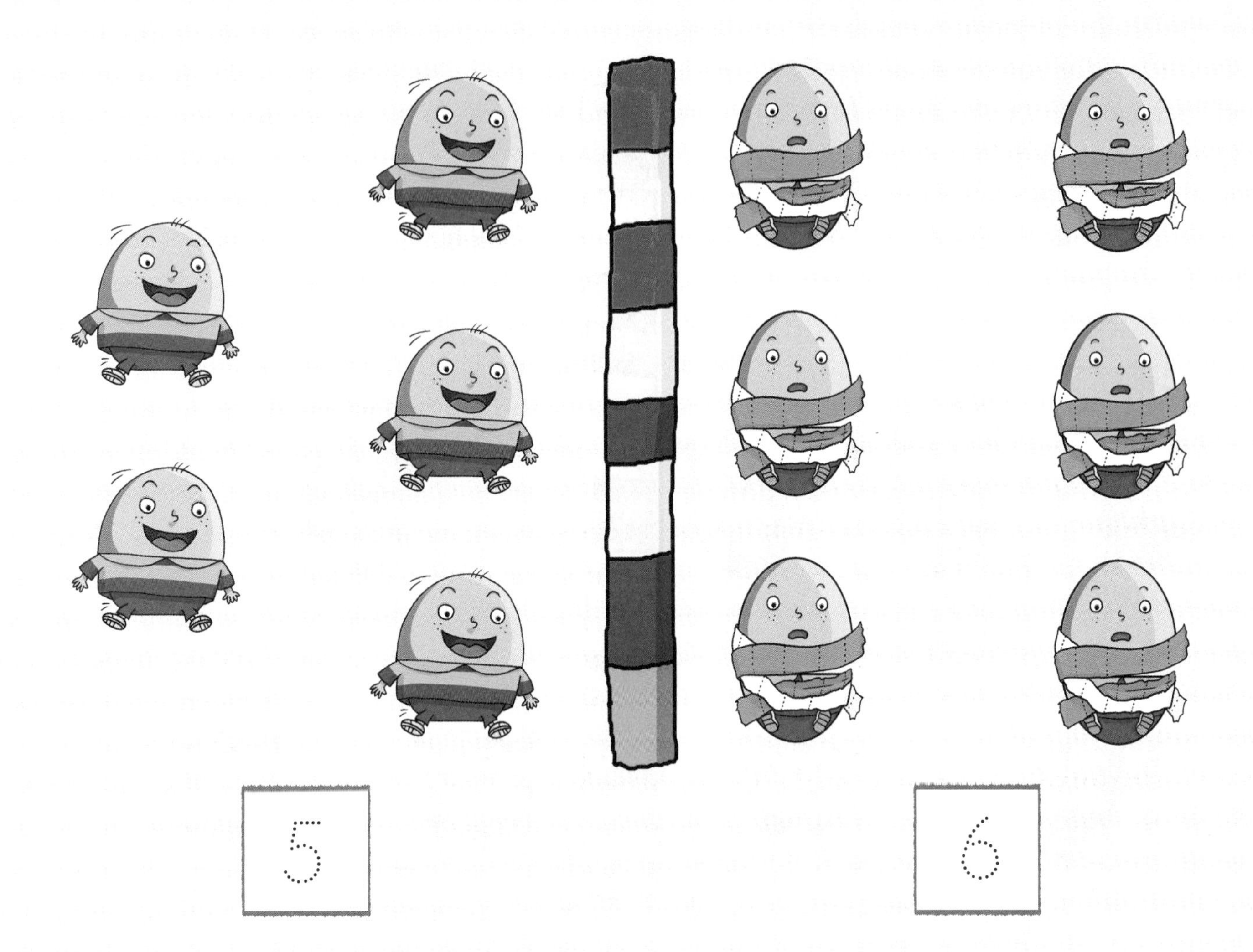

5 6

5 is less than 6 .

1 less

Count.
Write the numbers.

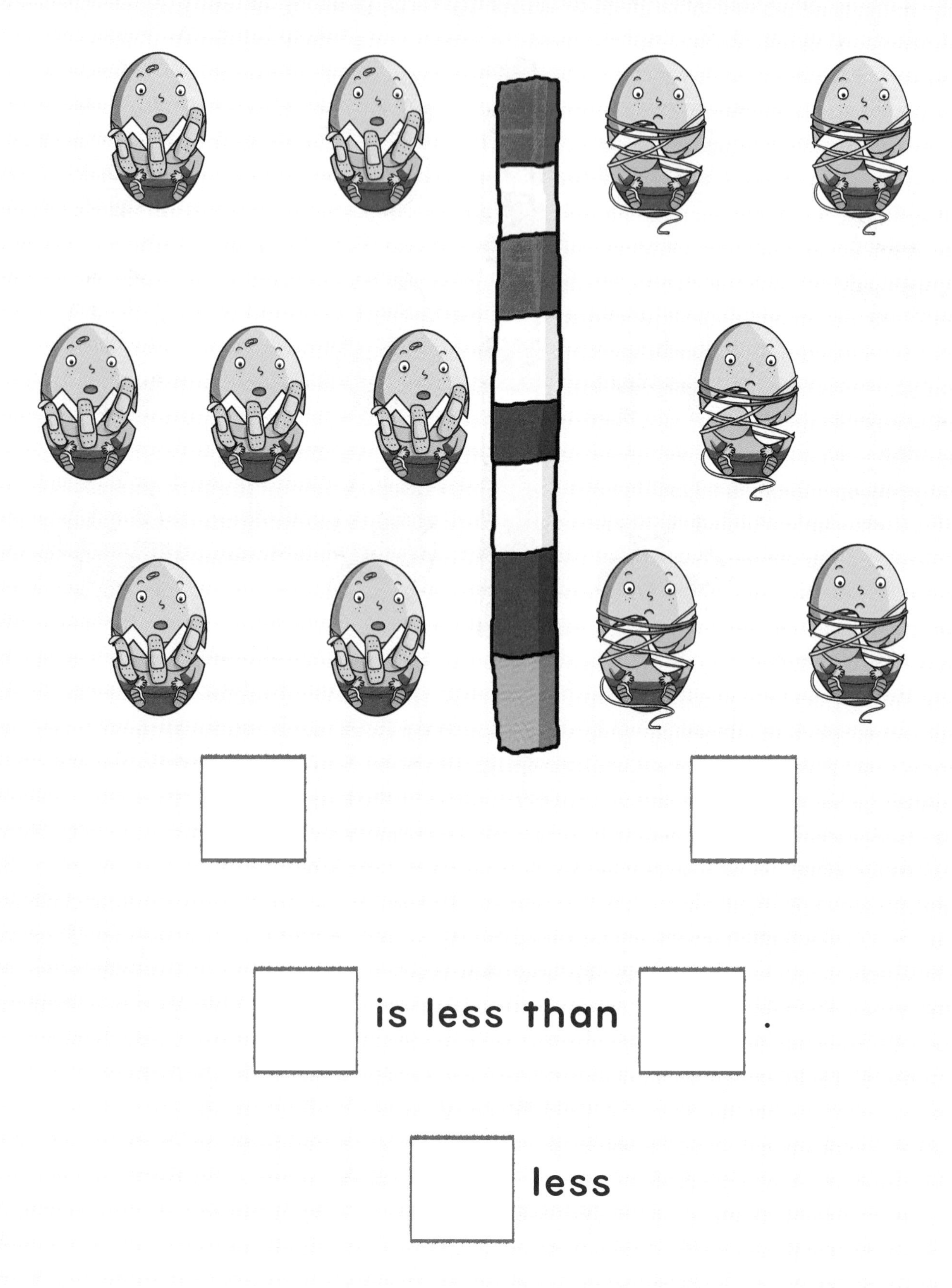

☐ is less than ☐ .

☐ less

Count.
Write the numbers.

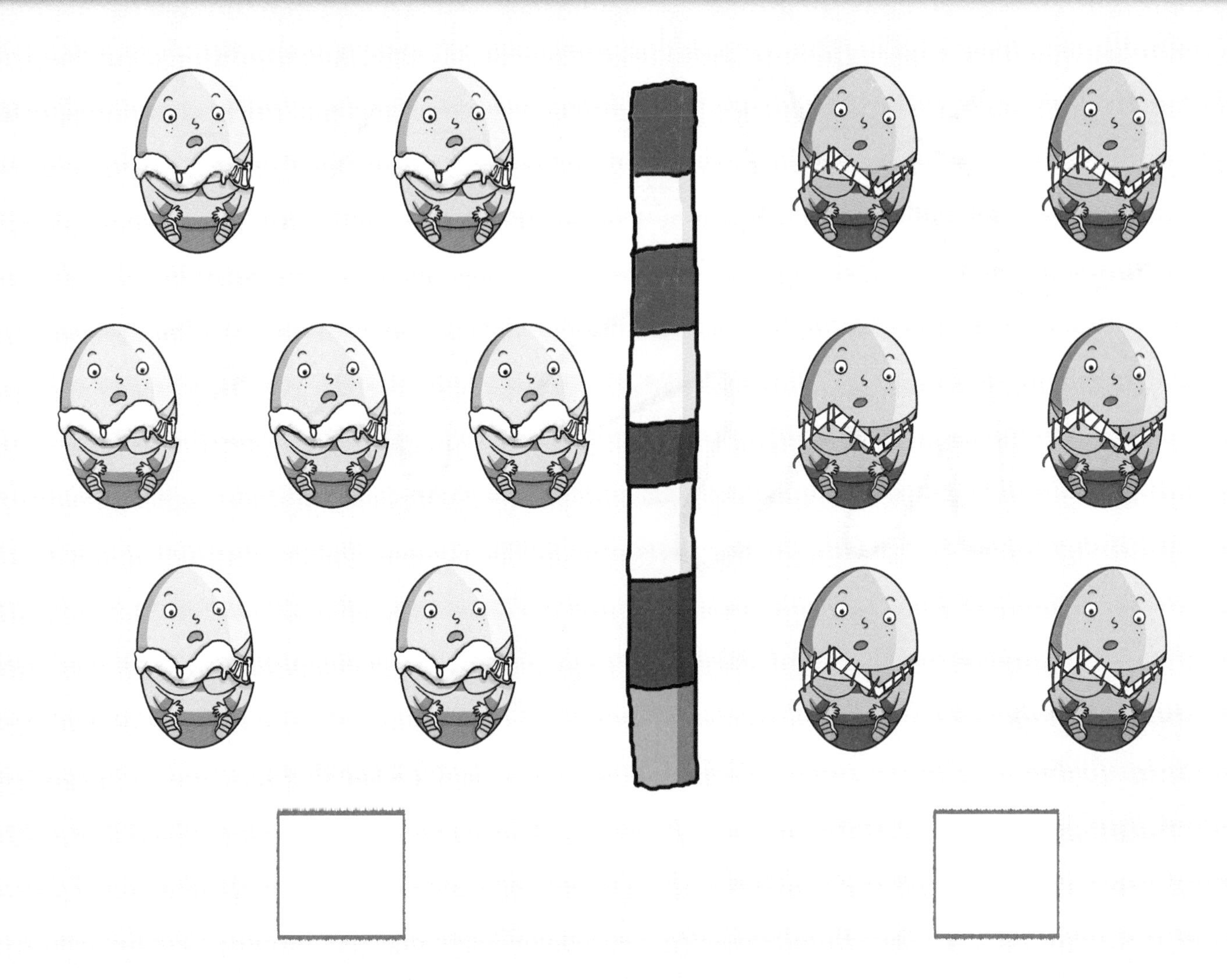

☐ ☐

☐ is less than ☐ .

☐ less

Activity

1

Count the beans.
Paste the cutouts.

Cutouts: Page 103

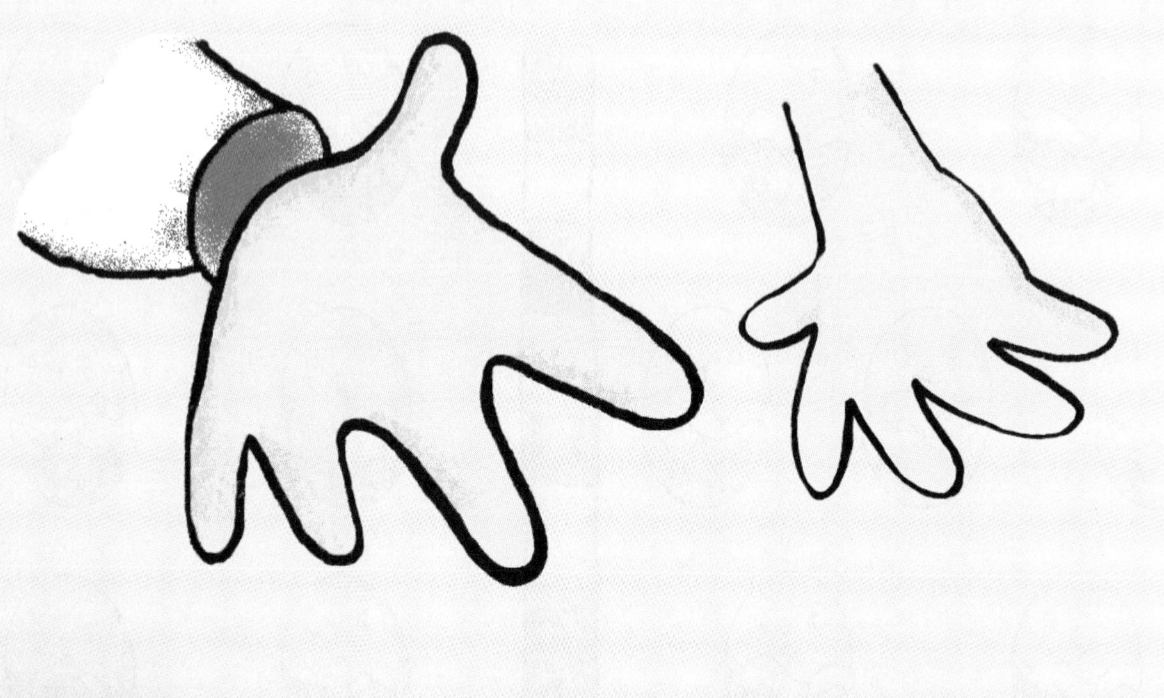

  and  make  .

  and  make  .

Note: Put beans of two colors in six containers — each container should contain 10 beans of one color and x (between 0 to 9) beans of another color. Distribute these to the students. Guide them to place ten beans of one color on the big open palm on this page and x beans of the other color on the small open palm, and count the total number of beans. Then, tell them to use the cutouts provided on page 103 for each sentence to show '[10] and [x] make [1x].'

Count the beans.
Paste the cutouts.

☐ and ☐ make ☐ .

☐ and ☐ make ☐ .

☐ and ☐ make ☐ .

☐ and ☐ make ☐ .

Activity 2

Paste the cutouts. Count. Write the numbers.

Cutouts: Pages 103 and 105

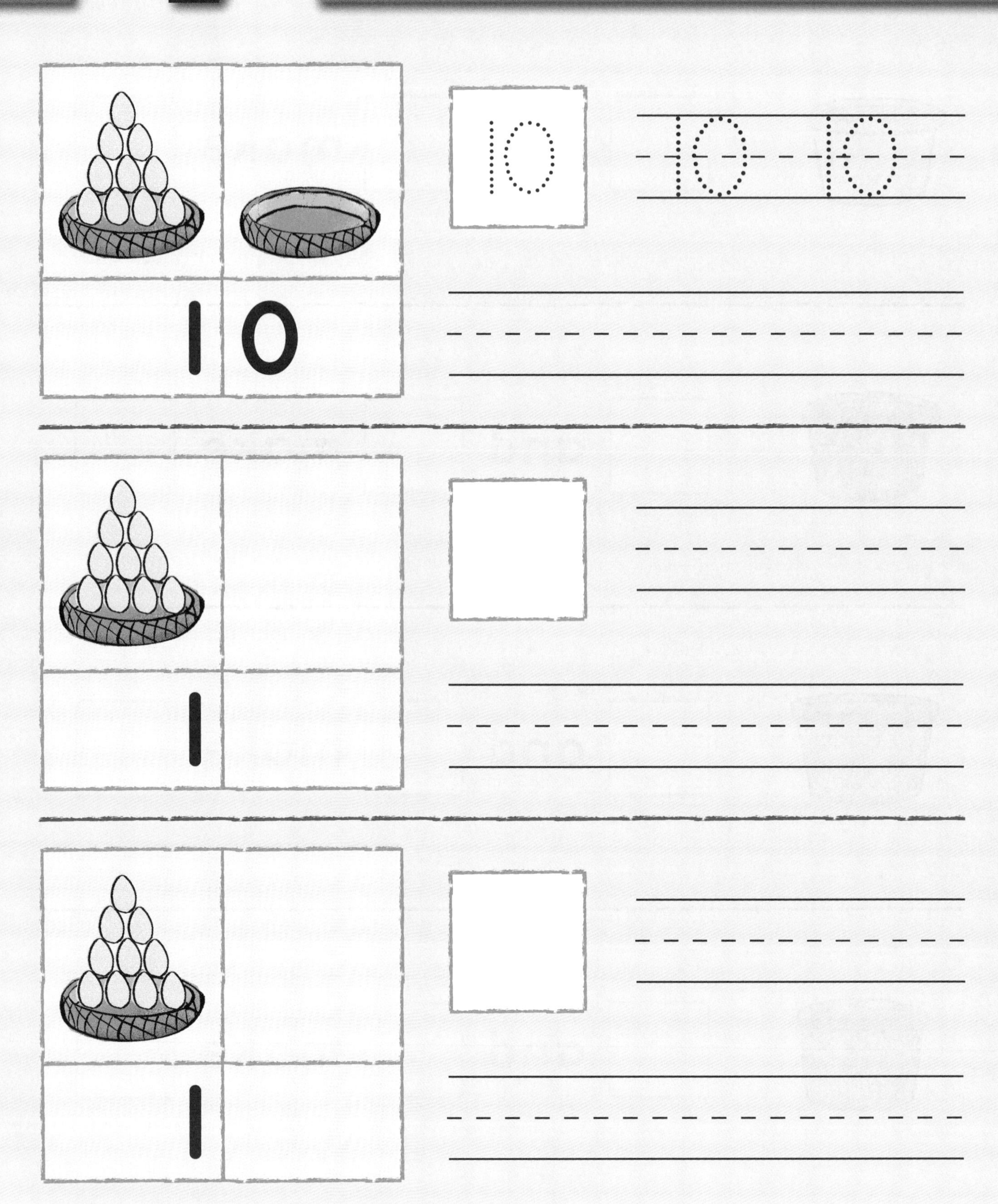

Paste the cutouts.
Count. Write the numbers.

1

1

1

Activity

3

Count.
Write the numbers.

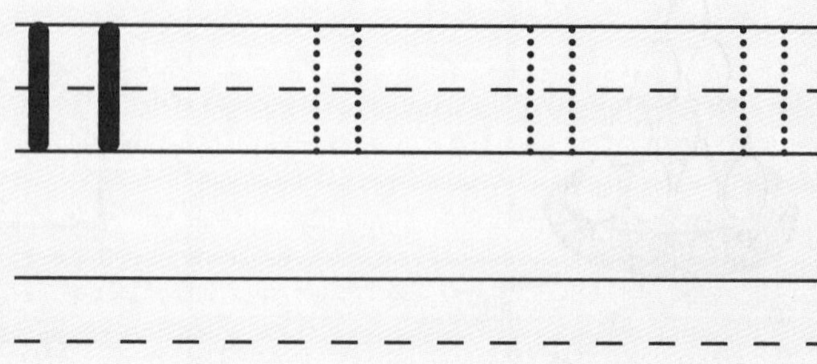

Count.
Write the numbers.

Count.
Write the numbers.

Activity

4

Slurp! Slurp Slurp! The giant gobbled up his supper.

Count! Count! Count!
Paste the cutouts.

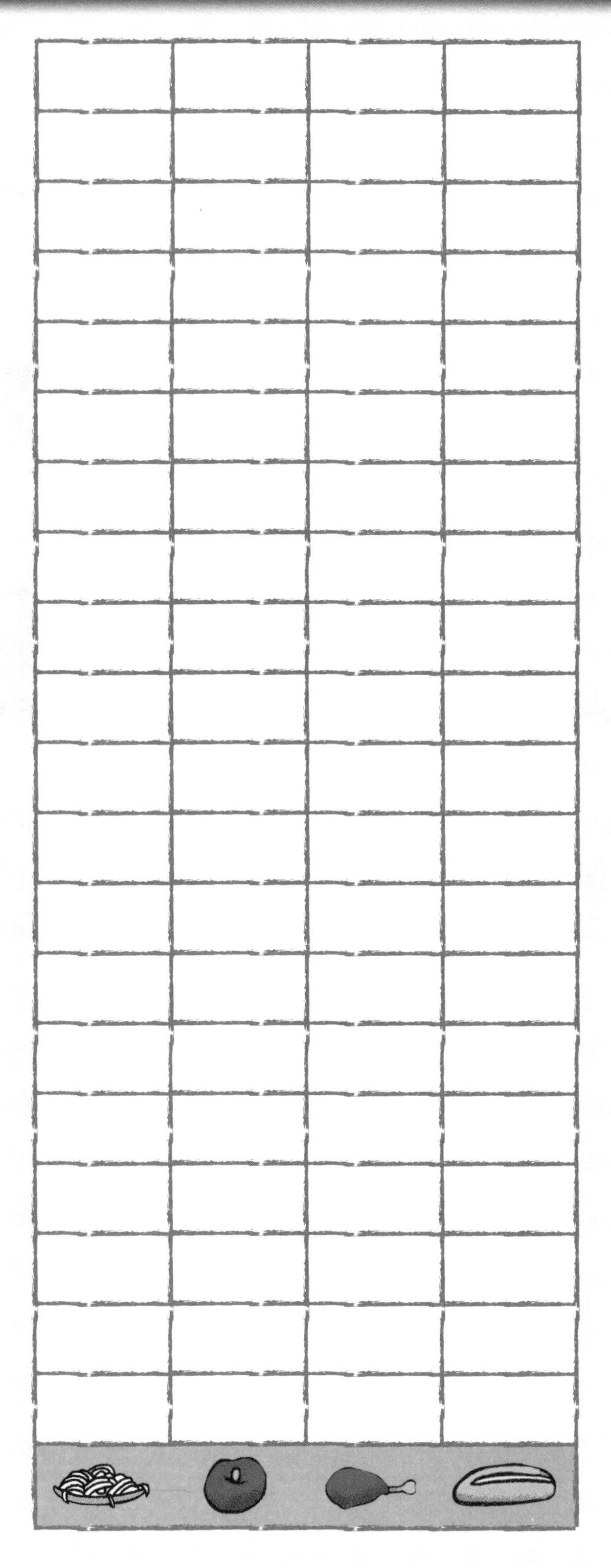

Activity

5 Play the game.

Note: In this card game for two players, the basic objective is for the players to pick out two consecutive numbers from number cards 1 to 20. The number cards are provided as cutouts on pages 107 and 109. At the start of the game, the number cards are placed faced down on a table. A player starts the game and uncovers any two number cards of choice. If they are consecutive number cards, he gets to keep the cards and has another turn. The game ends when all number cards on the table are non-consecutive. The player with more number cards wins the game.

Activity 1

Count the bags.
Write the numbers.

and make 3.

and make .

Count the bags.
Write the number.

and make ☐ .

Count the grass patches.
Write the number.

and make ☐ .

Count the grass patches.
Write the numbers.

and  make ☐ .

and make ☐ .

Activity

2 Count the sheep. Write the numbers.

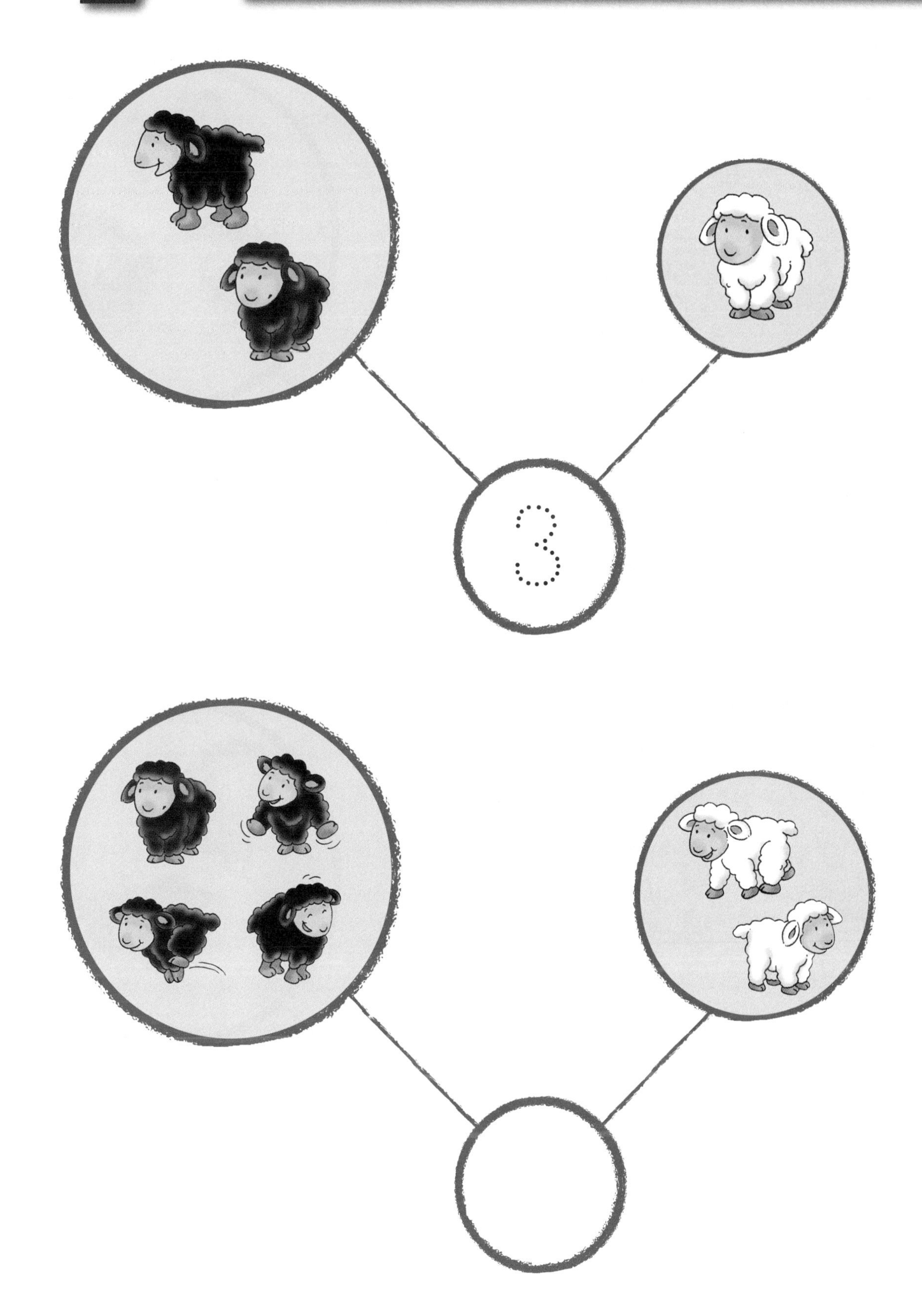

Count the sheep.
Write the numbers.

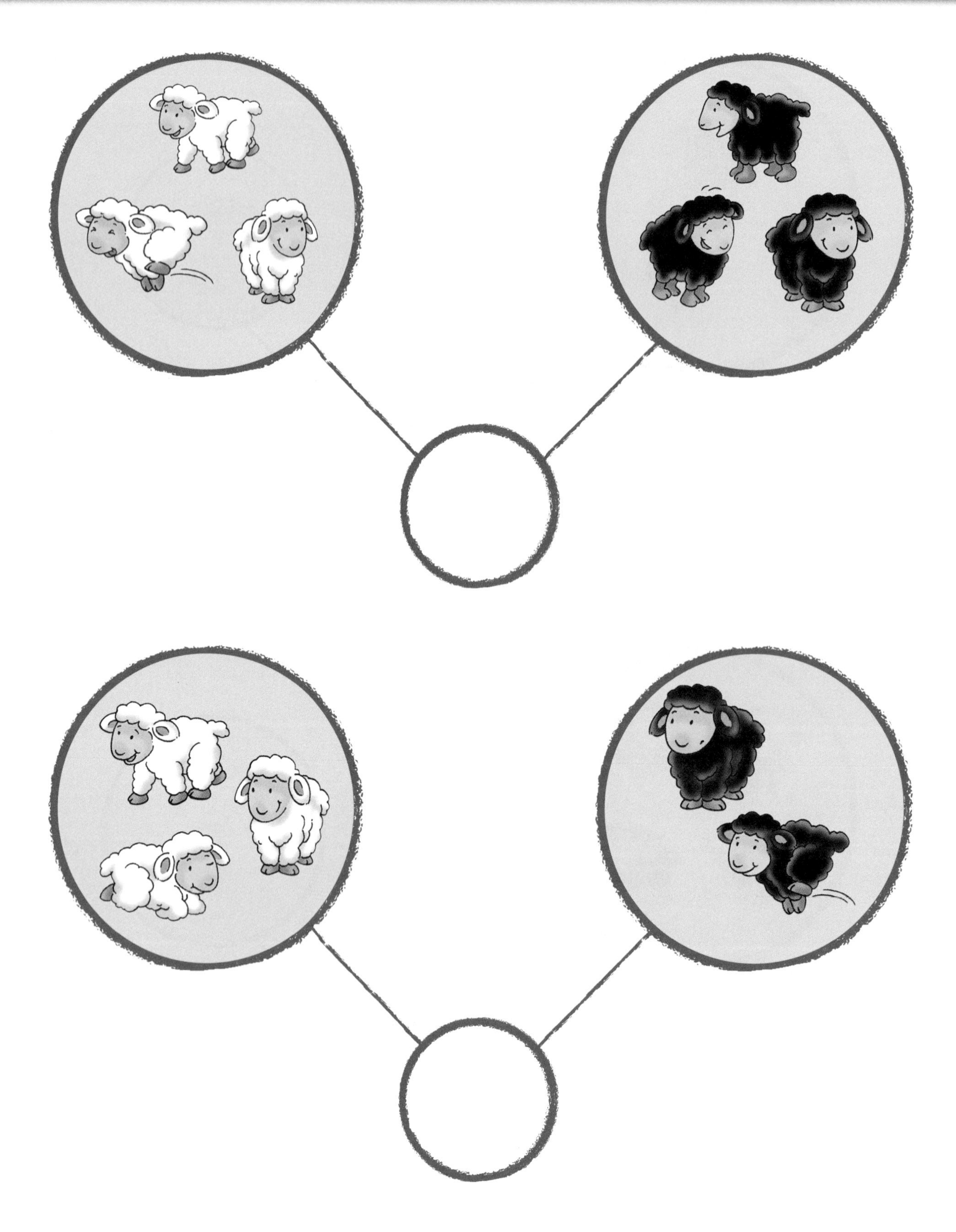

Count the bags.
Write the numbers.

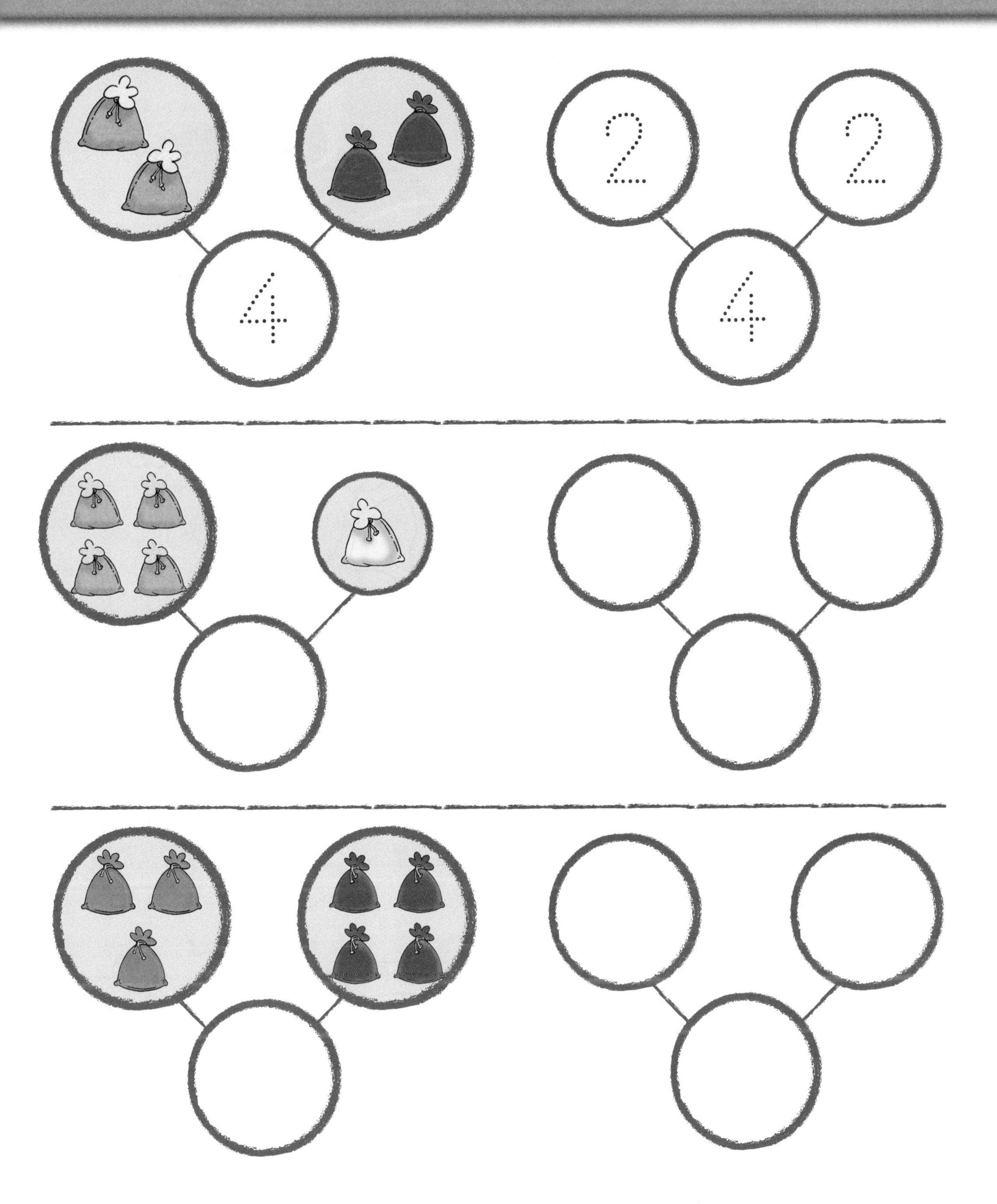

Activity

3

Color some blue. Color the rest red.

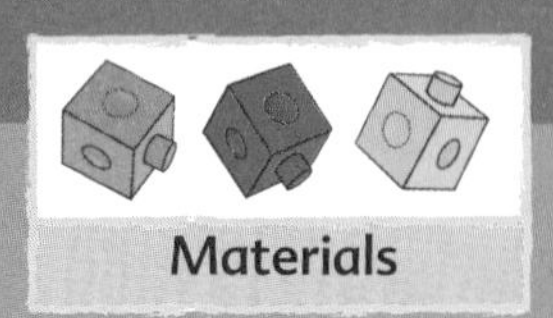

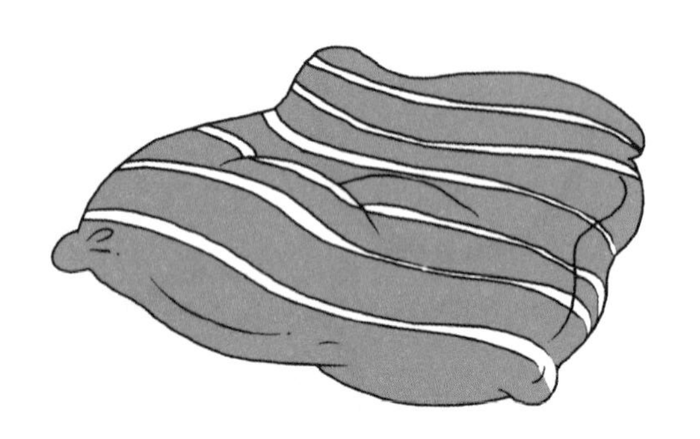
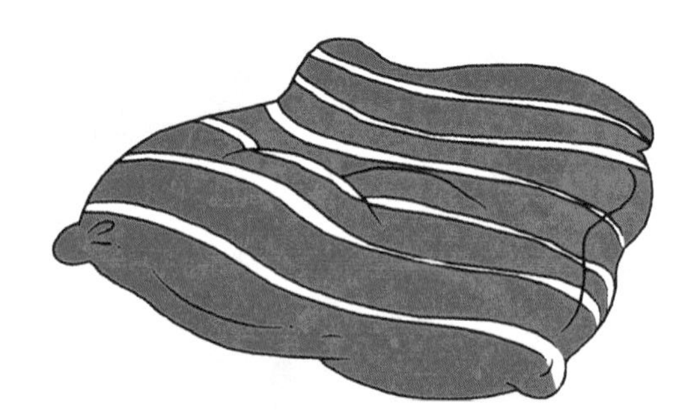

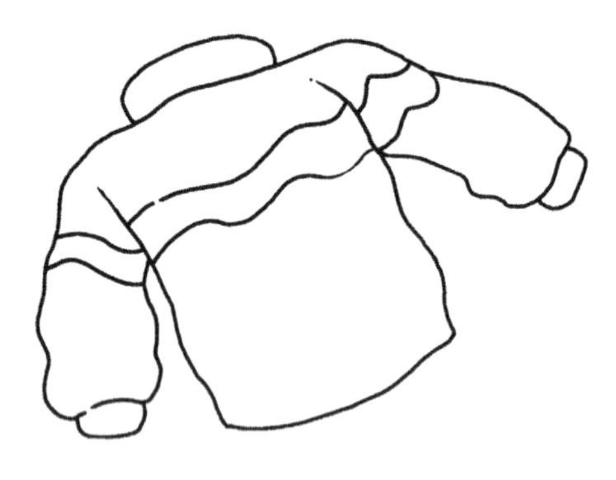
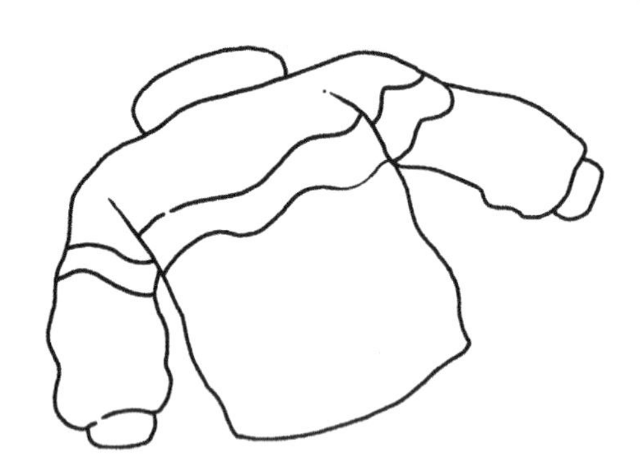

Color some sheep blue. Color the rest green. Write the numbers.

Color some sheep blue. Color the rest green. Write the numbers.

Activity

4 They share 7 bags of wool. Paste the cutouts.

Cutouts: Page 111

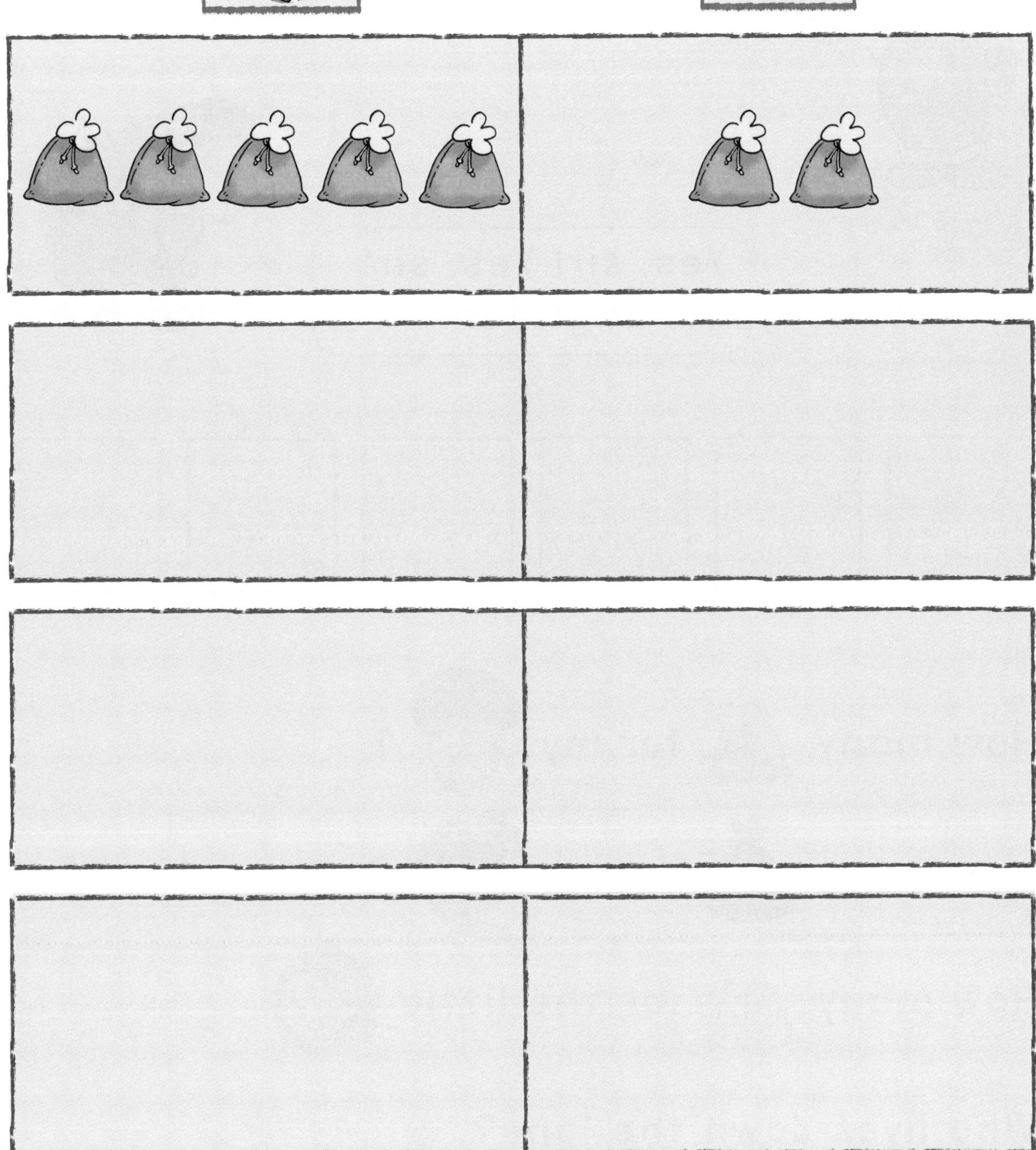

Activity

5 How many bags full?

Baa, baa, black sheep
Have you any wool?

Yes, sir! Yes, sir!
Six bags full.

How many  for my  ?

How many for my  ?

How many  for the little 

Who lives down the lane?

Color the bags.

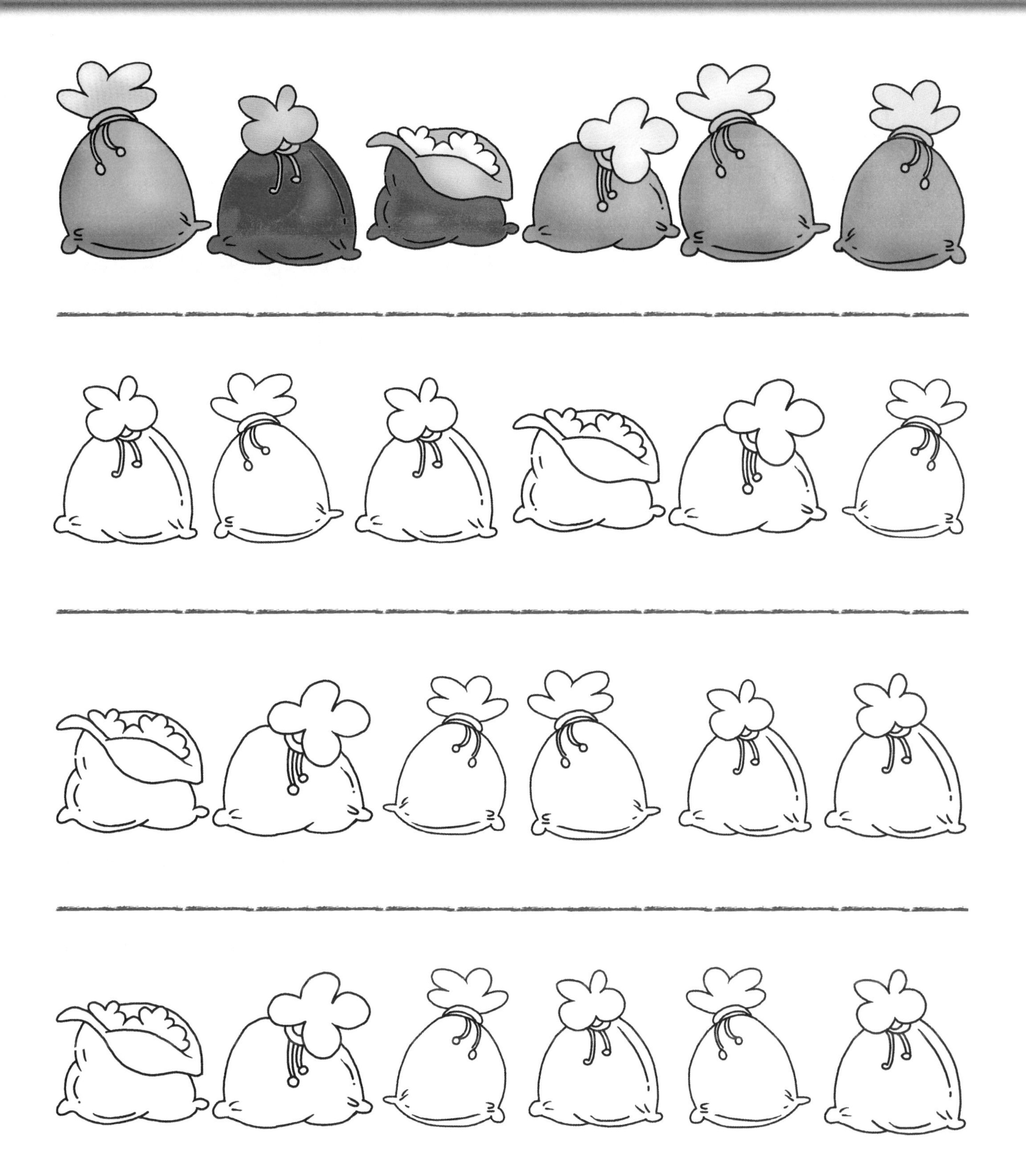

Activity 1

Count the birds. Write the numbers.

birds altogether.

birds altogether.

Count the birds.
Write the numbers.

☐ birds altogether.

☐ birds altogether.

Count the birds.
Write the numbers.

☐ birds altogether.

☐ birds altogether.

Activity

2

Add.
Write the numbers.

$1 + 1 = $ 2

$1 + 2 = $ ☐

Add.
Write the numbers.

3 + 1 = ☐

Activity

3

Listen to the rhyme. Add. Write the numbers.

Cutouts: Page 115

3 little dicky birds,
Sitting on the wall.
2 more came
To join them all.

birds altogether.

---

2 little dicky birds,
Sitting on the wall.
4 more came
To join them all.

☐ birds altogether.

Note: Have students make use of the cutouts of flying birds on page 115 to add as they listen to the rhyme.

Listen to the rhyme.
Add. Write the numbers.

4 little dicky birds,
Sitting on the wall.
3 more came
To join them all.

☐ birds altogether.

3 little dicky birds,
Sitting on the wall.
3 more came
To join them all.

 birds altogether.

Listen to the rhyme.
Add. Write the numbers.

5 little dicky birds,
Sitting on the wall.
3 more came
To join them all.

☐ birds altogether.

---

6 little dicky birds,
Sitting on the wall.
4 more came
To join them all.

☐ birds altogether.

Activity

4

Complete the .
Write the number sentence.

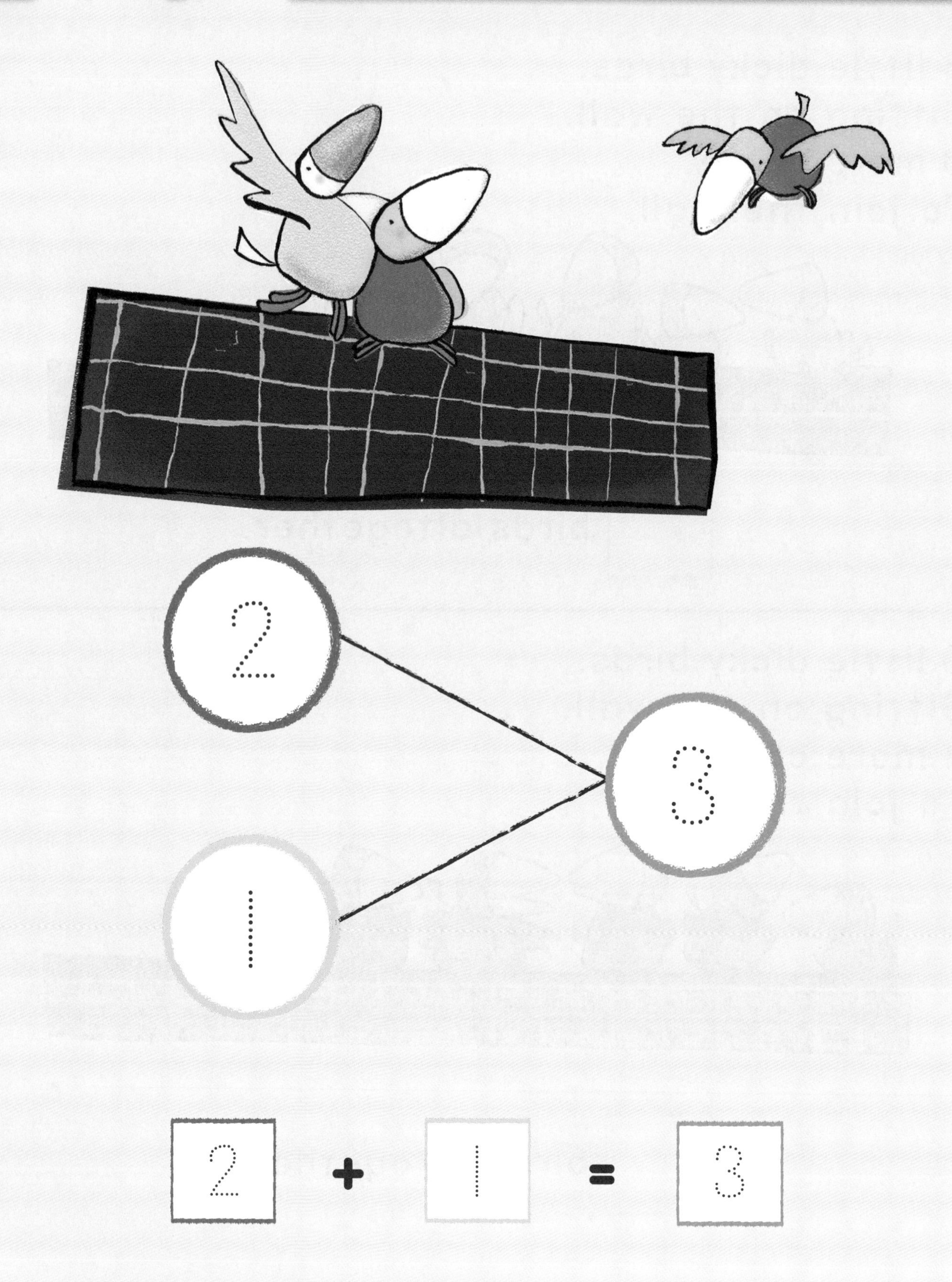

Complete the number bond. Write the number sentence.

Complete the number bond. Write the number sentence.

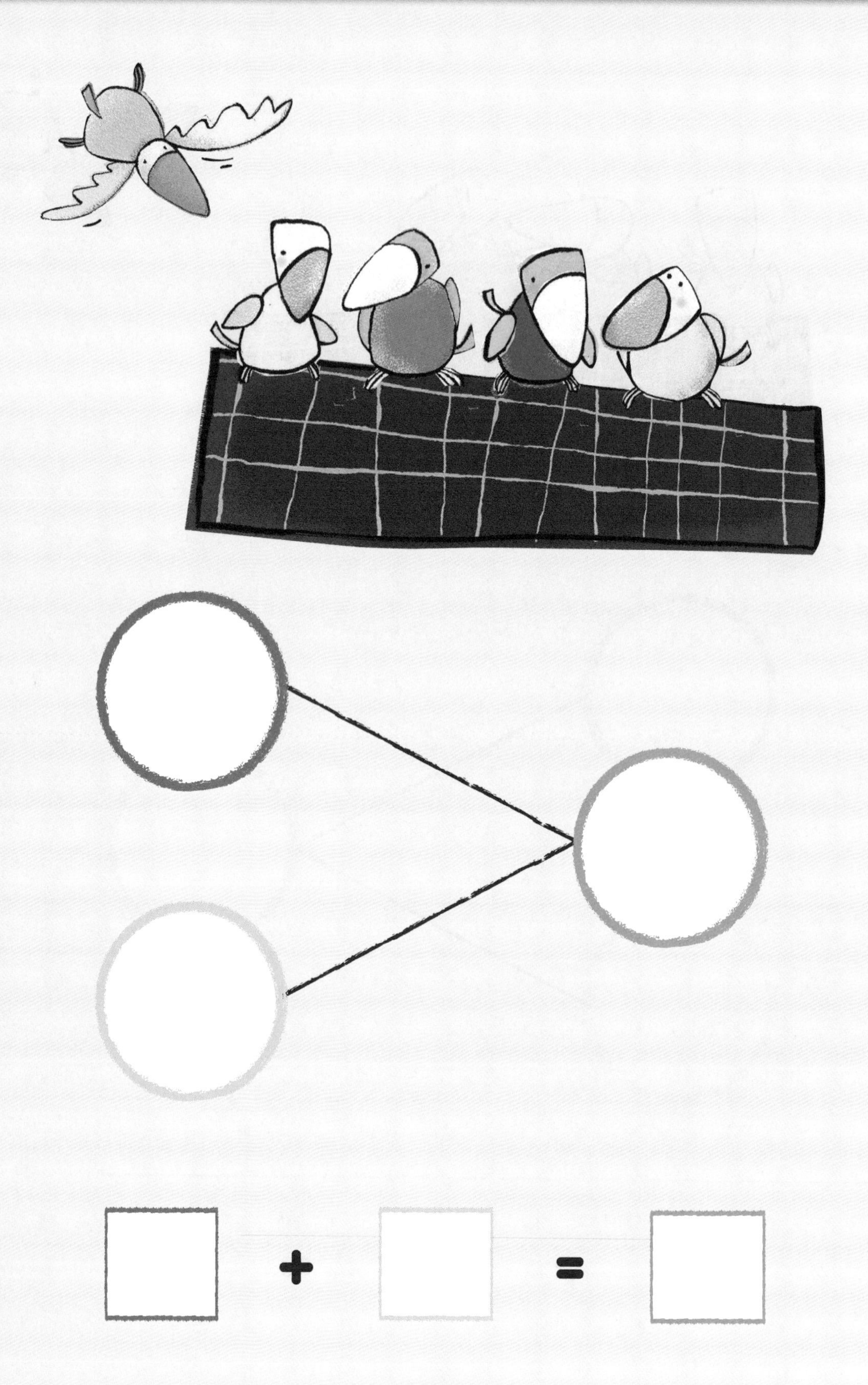

Complete the number bond.
Write the number sentence.

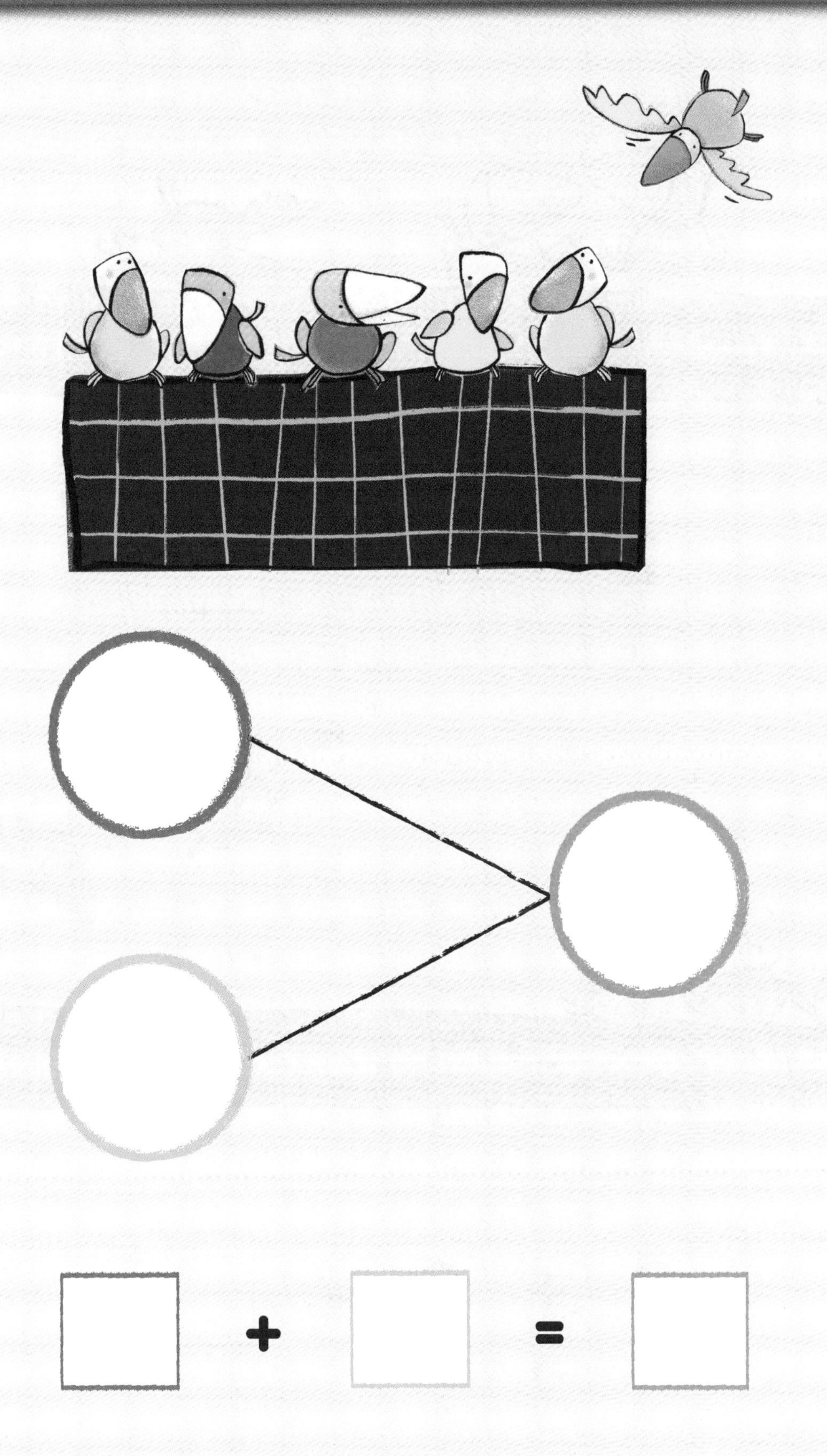

$\square + \square = \square$

Cutouts: Page 115

Activity

5

Add.
Write the numbers.

2 + 1 = 3

3 + 2 = ☐

How many little dicky birds sitting on the wall? How many came to join them all?

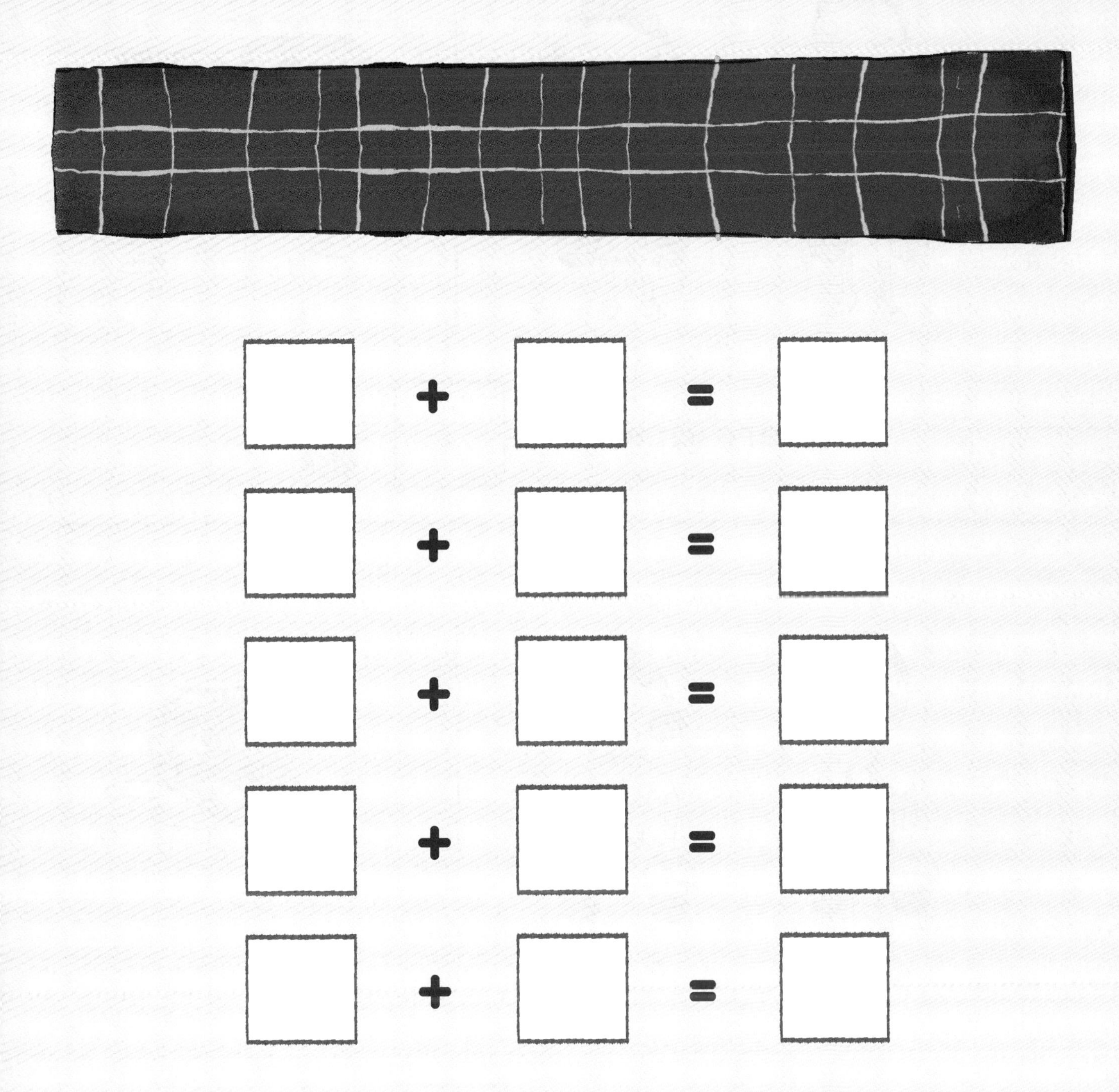

Note: Guide students to use the cutouts on page 115 to form number sentences.

Activity 1

Subtract.
Write the numbers.

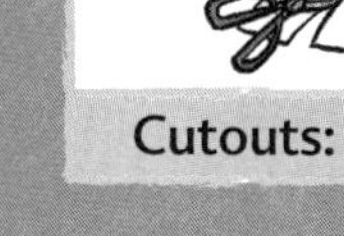

Cutouts: Page 117

There are still  .

There are still  .

Subtract.
Write the numbers.

There are still ☐ 🪣.

There are still ☐ 🪣.

Activity

2 Read the rhyme. Write the numbers.

Cutouts: Page 117

Jack and Jill
Went up the hill
To fetch .

Jack carried .

How many  did Jill carry?

Jack and Jill
Went up the hill
To fetch .

Jill carried .

How many  did Jack carry?

Read the rhyme.
Write the numbers.

Jack and Jill
Went up the hill

To fetch 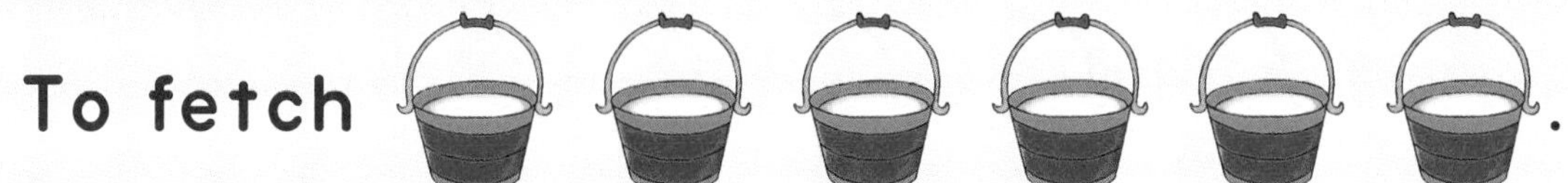      .

Jack carried    .

How many  did Jill carry?  

Jack and Jill
Went up the hill

To fetch  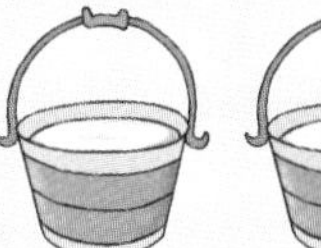  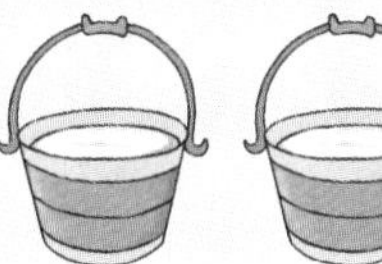 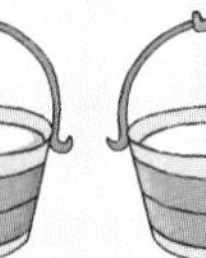 .

Jill carried .

How many  did Jack carry?  

Activity 3

Read the rhyme.
Write the number sentences.

Jack and Jill
Went up the hill
To fetch .

Jack used .

There is still 1 .

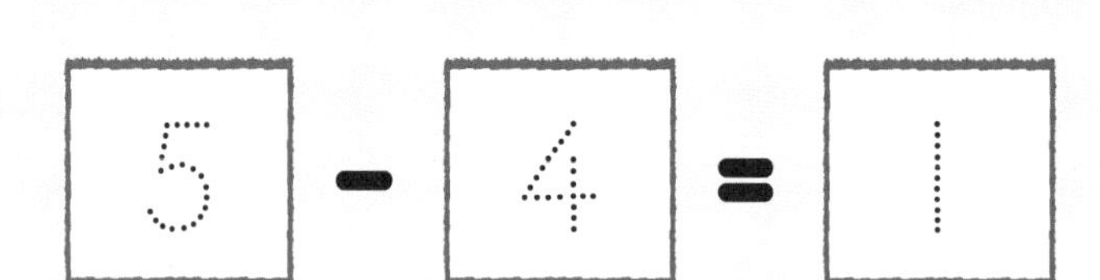

Jack and Jill
Went up the hill
To fetch .

Jill used .

There are still ☐ .

Read the rhyme.
Write the number sentences.

Jack and Jill
Went up the hill
To fetch .

Jack used to .

There are still .

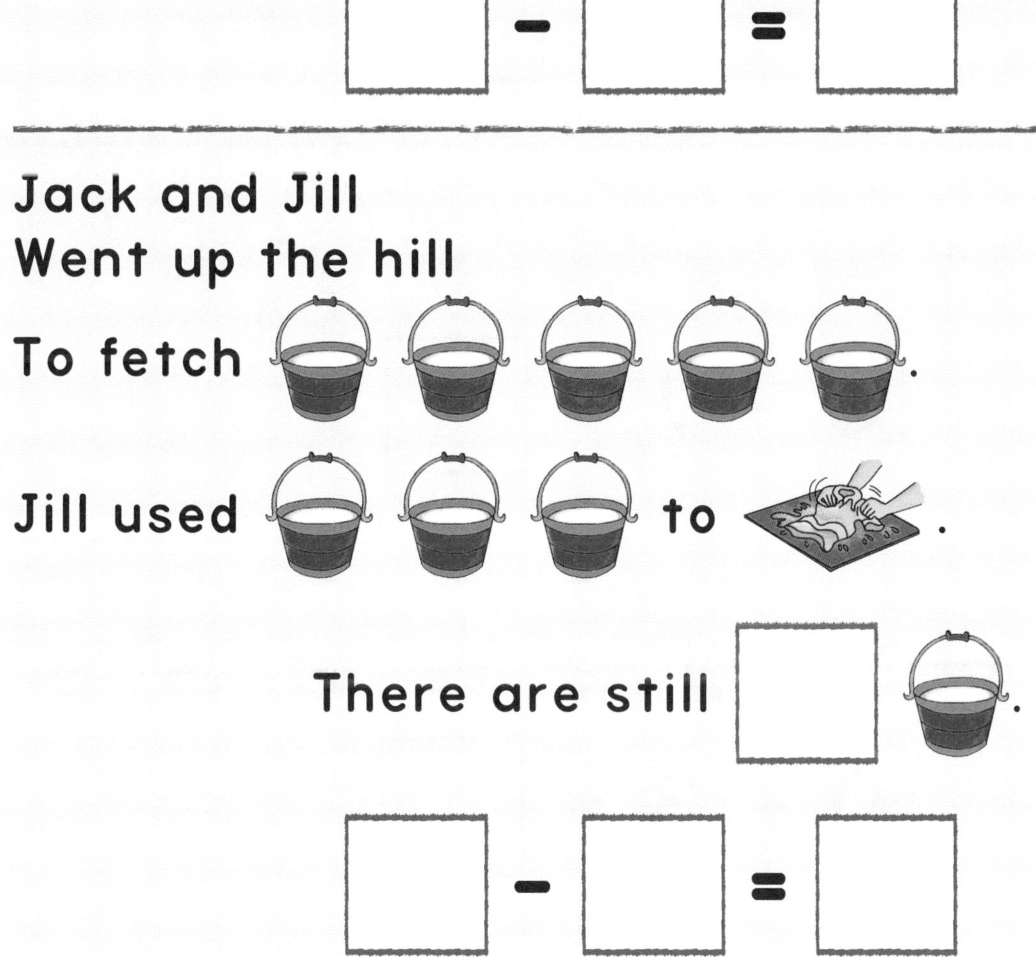

Jack and Jill
Went up the hill
To fetch .

Jill used to .

There are still .

Activity

Subtract.
Write the numbers.

Cutouts: Page 117

8 - 2 = 6

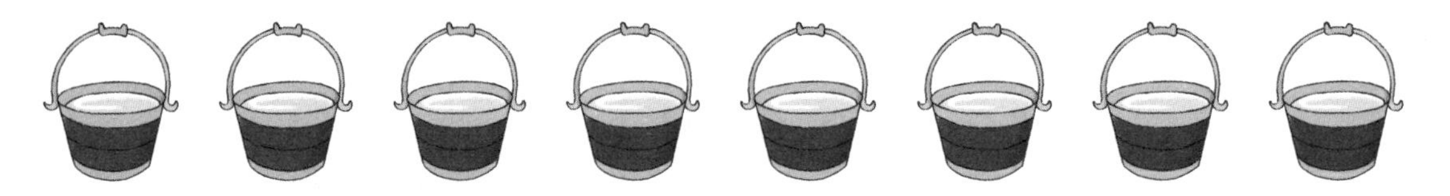

8 - 6 = ☐

---

10 - 7 = ☐

---

10 - 3 = ☐

Activity
5 Subtract and match.

Cutouts: Page 117

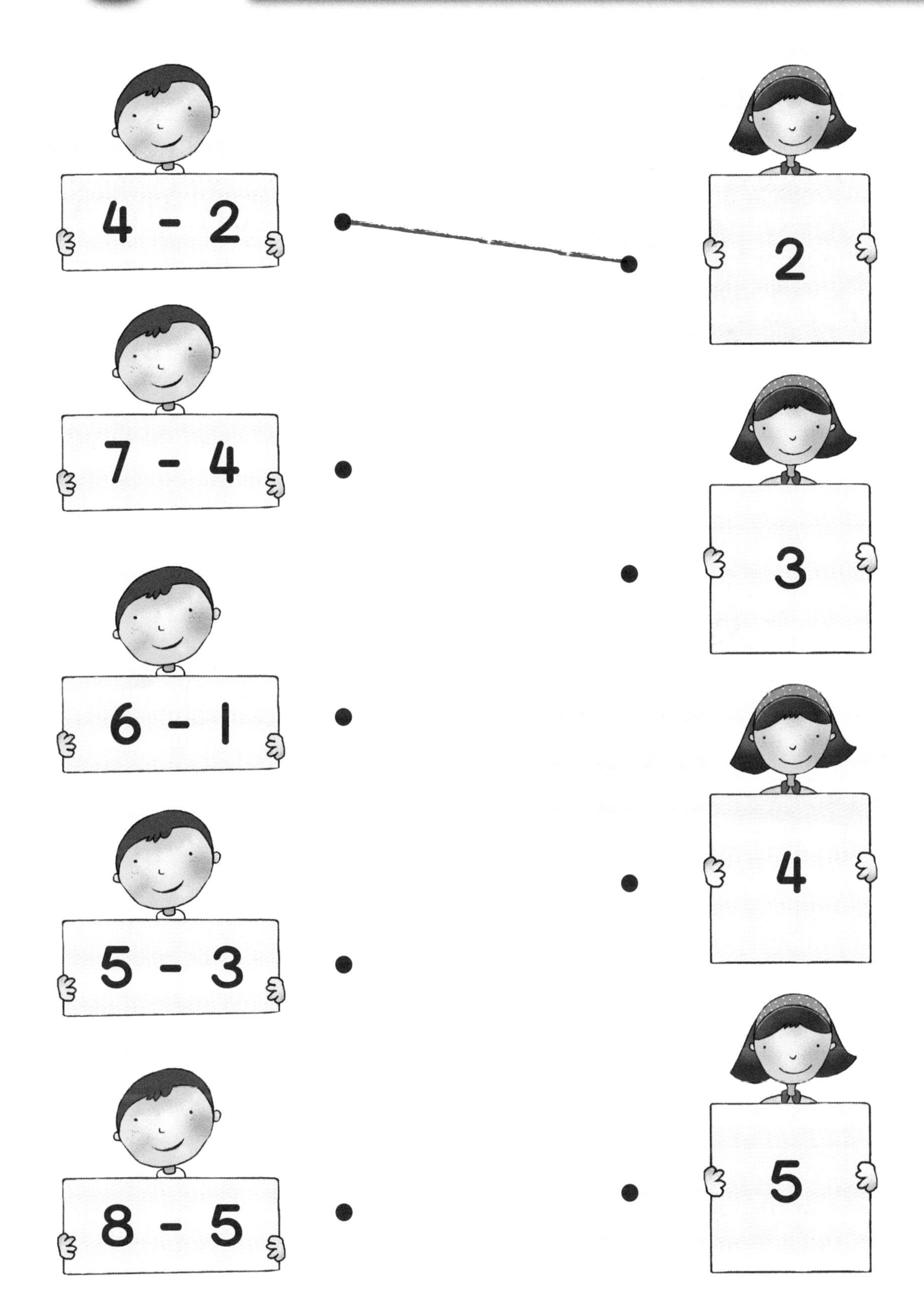

Activity

Subtract.
Complete the number sentences.

2 little dicky birds,
Sitting on the wall.

2 - ☐ = ☐

1 - ☐ = ☐

Add.
Complete the number sentences.

Activity

2

Add and subtract. Complete the number sentences.

Cutouts: Page 119

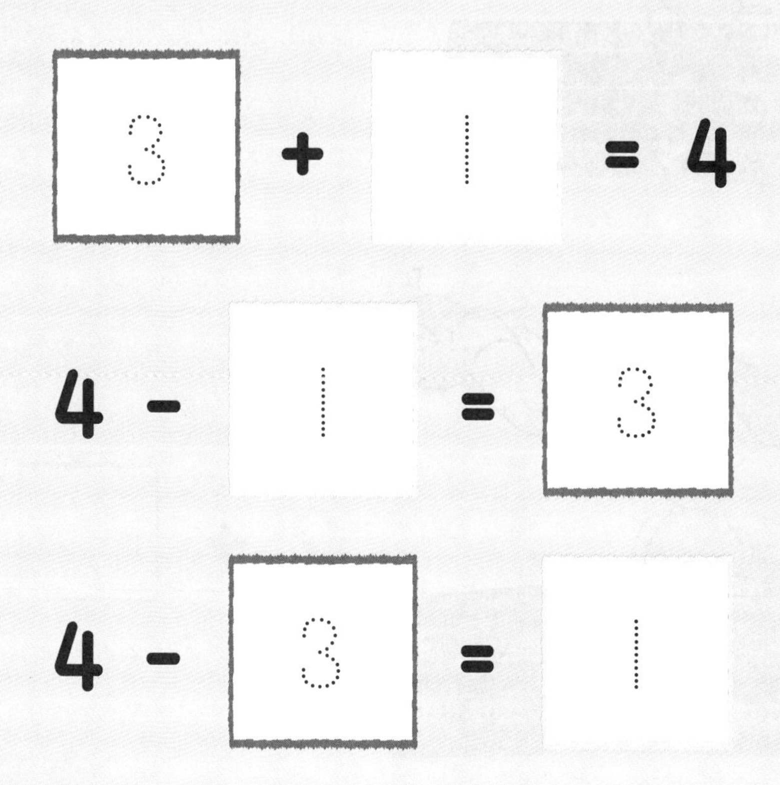

Add and subtract.
Complete the number sentences.

$\square + \square = 5$

$5 - \square = \square$

$5 - \square = \square$

Cutouts: Page 119

Activity 3

One little dicky bird, Sitting in a tree ...

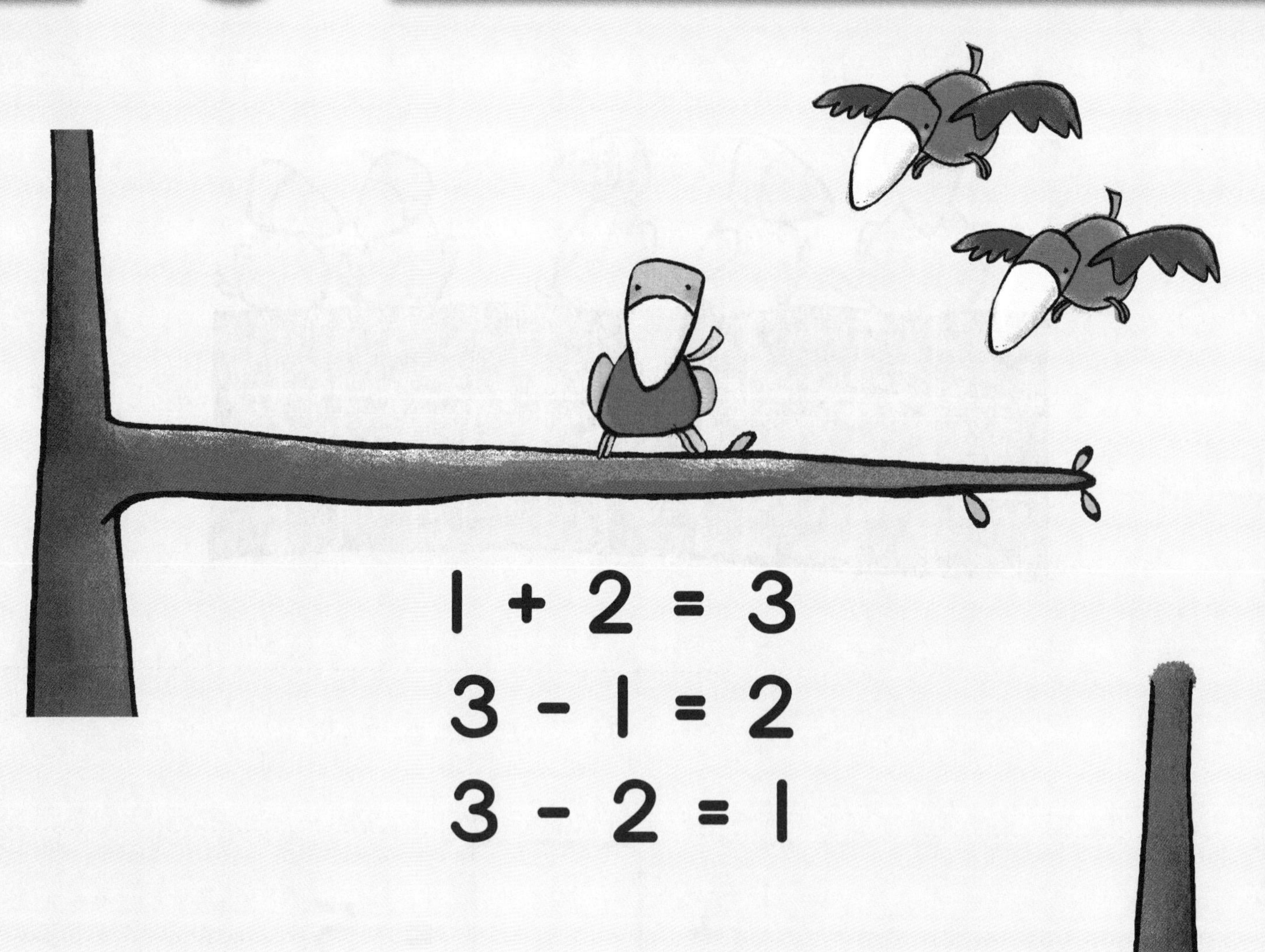

Note: Guide students to make use of the tree branch and cutouts of birds on page 119 to form different number sentences.

Add and subtract.
Write the number sentences.

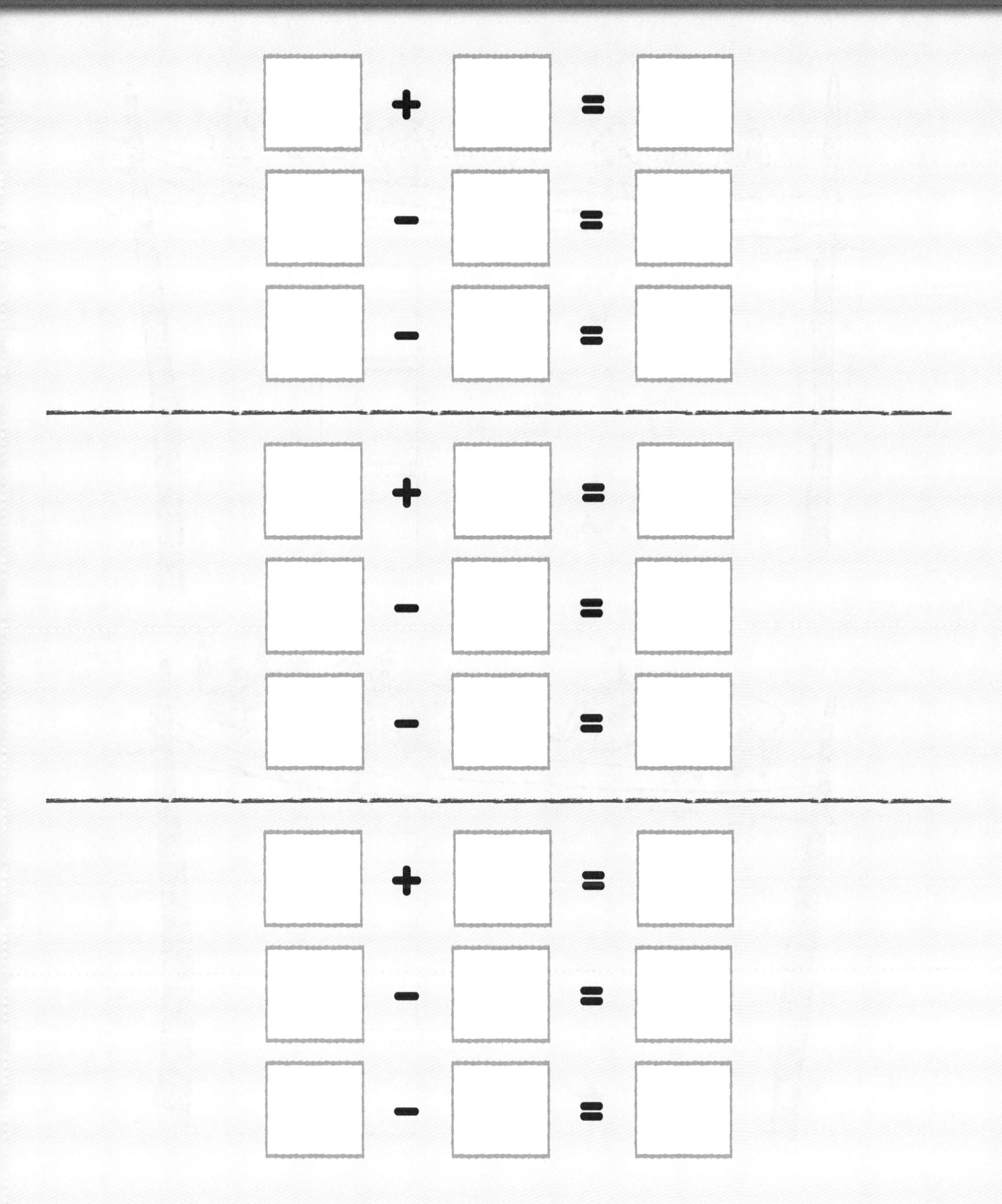

Activity

Add and subtract. Write the numbers.

Cutouts: Page 119

$7 - 3 = 4$

$7 - 4 = 3$

$3 + 4 = 7$

$9 - 6 =$ ____

$9 - 3 =$ ____

$6 + 3 =$ ____

Add and subtract.
Write the numbers.

$8 - 3 =$ ☐

$8 - 5 =$ ☐

$3 + 5 =$ ☐

$10 - 7 =$ ☐

$10 - 3 =$ ☐

$7 + 3 =$ ☐

Activity

5

Paste the cutouts.
Form number sentences.

Cutouts: Page 121

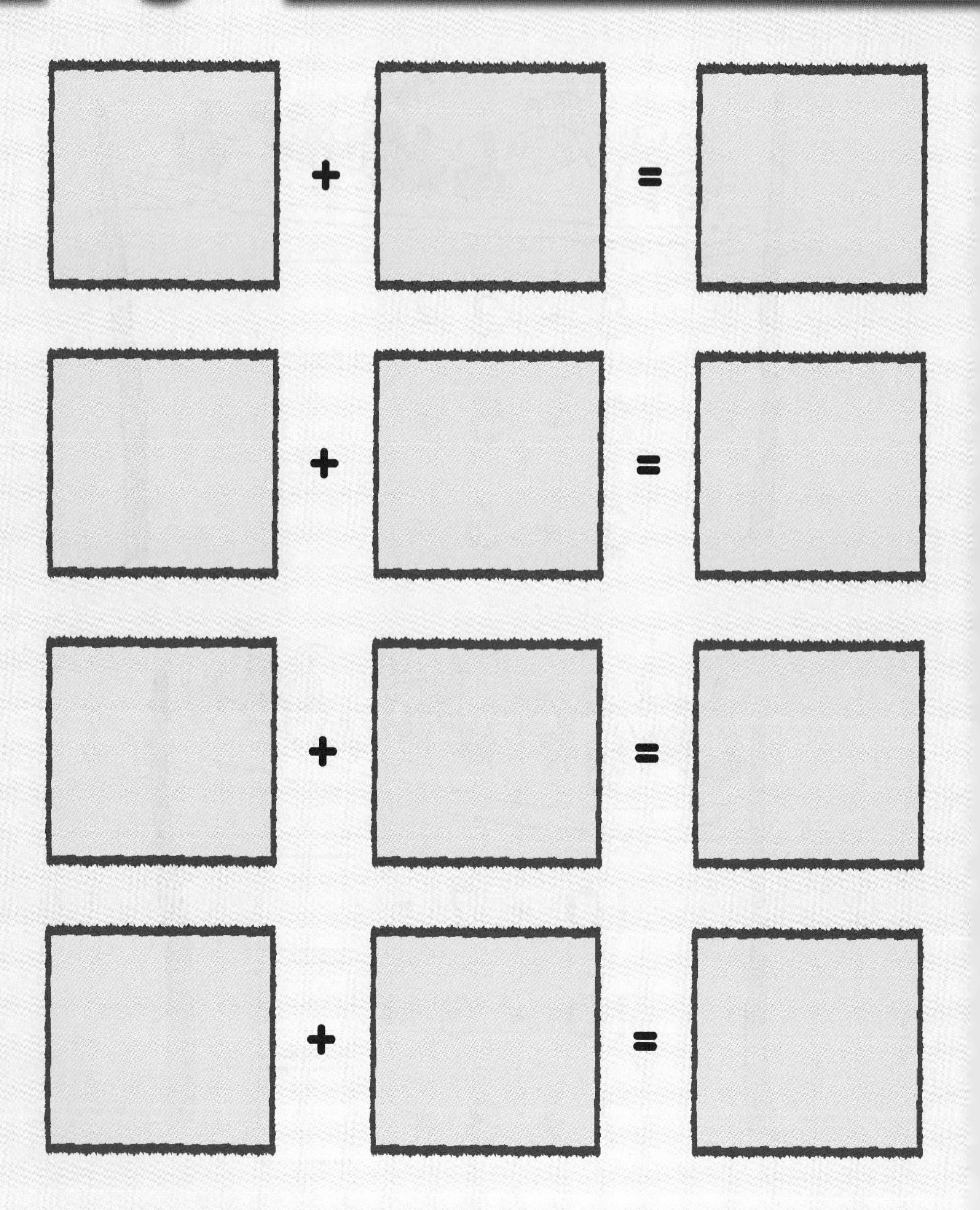

Activity

1 Count the beans. Paste the cutouts.

Cutouts: Page 123

Note: Put beans of two colors in six containers — each container should contain 20 beans of one color and x (between 0 to 9) beans of another color. Distribute these to the students. Guide them to place ten beans of one color on each of the two big open palms on this page and x beans of the other color on the small open palm, and count the total number of beans. Then, tell them to use the cutouts provided on page 123 for each sentence to obtain '20 and x make 2x.'

Count the beans.
Paste the cutouts.

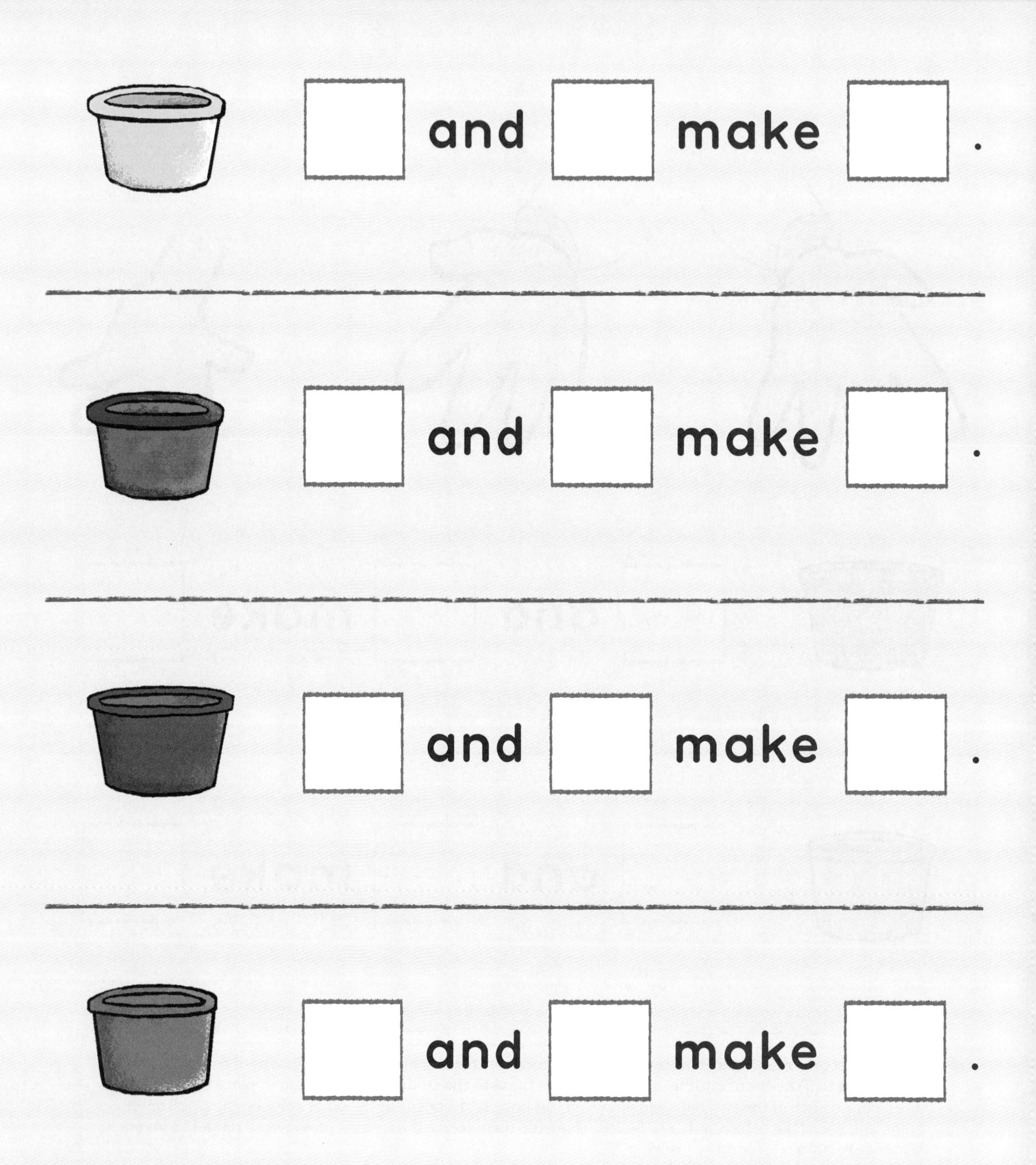

Activity

2

Paste the cutouts.
Count. Write the numbers.

Cutouts: Pages 123 and 125

20

20 20

2 0

2

2

Paste the cutouts.
Count. Write the numbers.

2

2

2

Activity

3 Play the game.

Cutouts: Pages 125 to 129

Note: In this card game for two players, the basic objective is for the players to pick out two consecutive numbers from number cards 1 to 30. The number cards are provided as cutouts. At the start of the game, the number cards are placed faced down on a table. A player starts the game and uncovers any two number cards of choice. If they are consecutive number cards, he gets to keep the cards and has another turn. The game ends when all number cards on the table are non-consecutive. The player with more number cards wins the game.

Activity

Play Snakes and Ladders!

Climb the ladder!
Show the correct number at each end of the ladder.

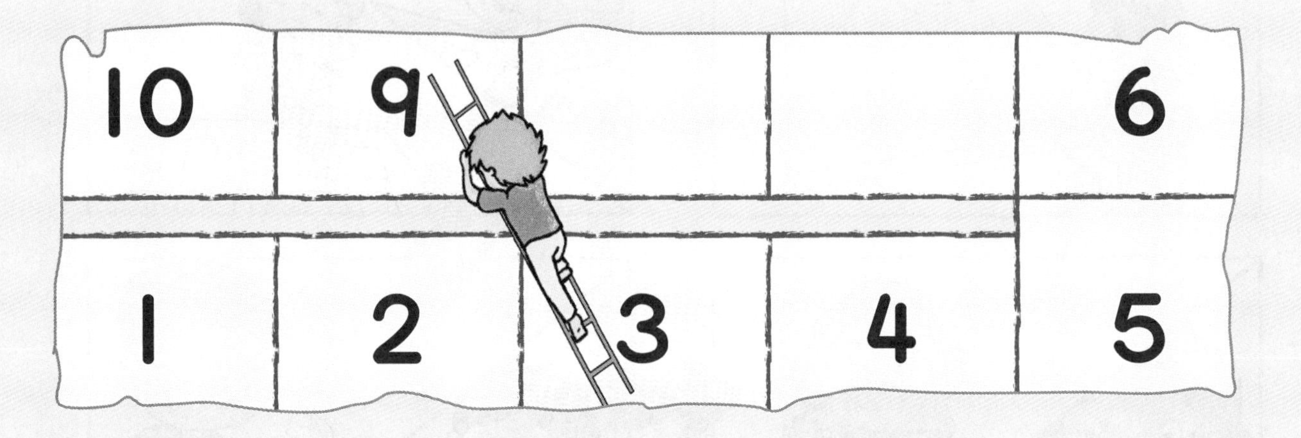

Make your friend slide down the snake!
Show the correct numbers at its head and tail.

Note: To climb up the ladder or make their friend slide down the snake, students have to show the numbers at both ends of the ladder or snake respectively using the cutouts provided on page 131. Allow them to show consecutive numbers, e.g. they can show the numbers 13 and 14 in showing the number at the tail end of the purple snake connecting the 14 and 16 number squares.

Show the correct numbers.

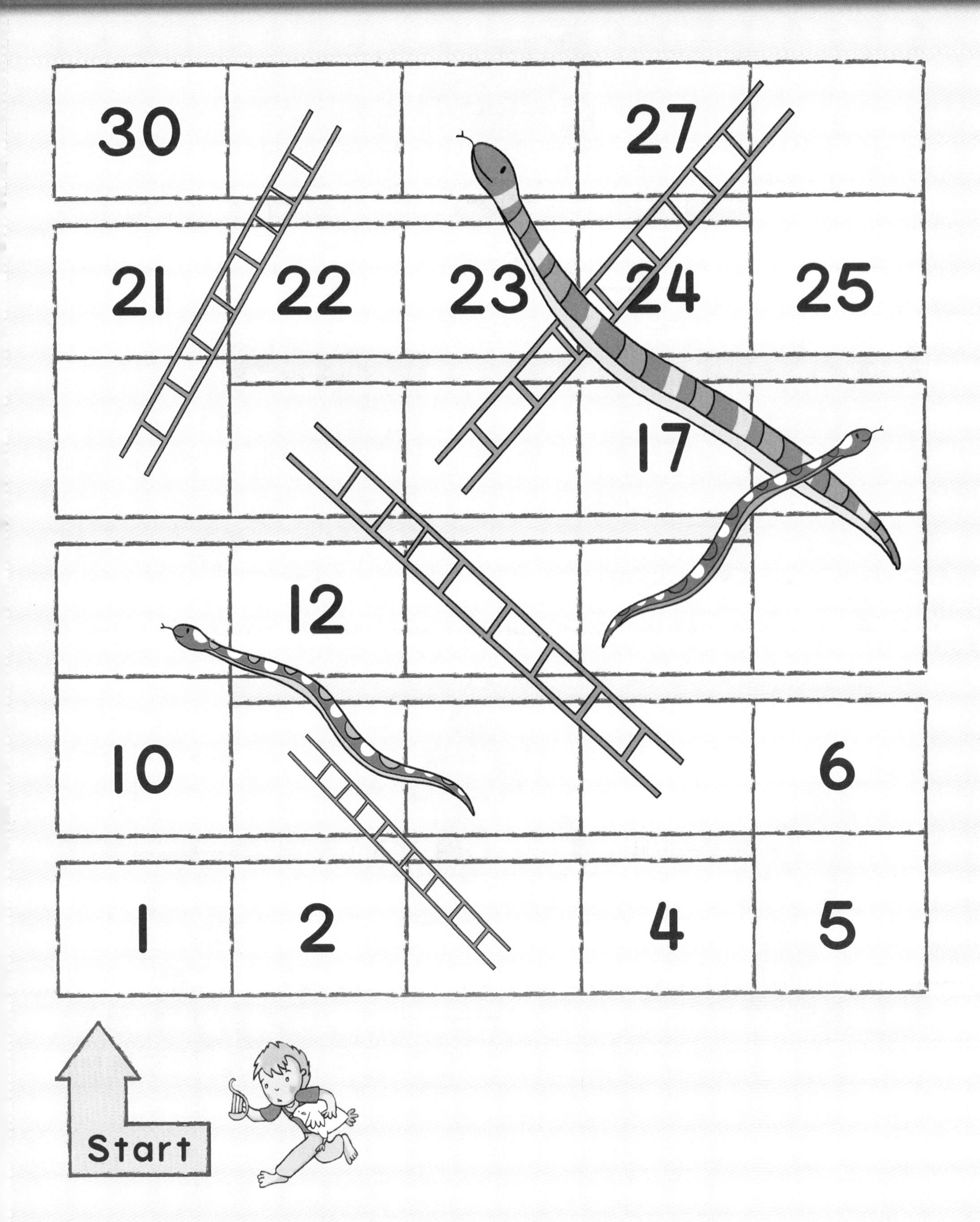

Activity 1

Put in order. Write the numbers.

Cutouts: Page 133

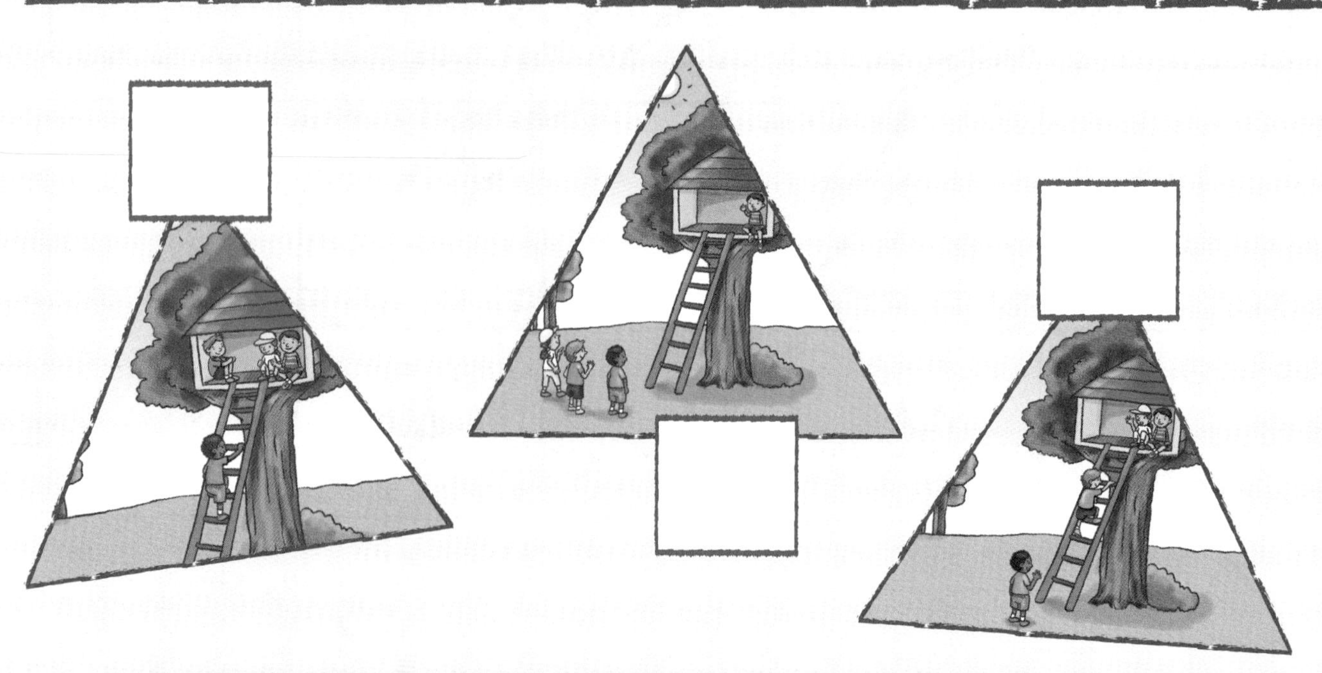

Note: For each task, have students sequence the cutouts correctly before they write the numbers.

Put in order.
Write the numbers.

Activity

2

Tell the time.
Write the numbers.

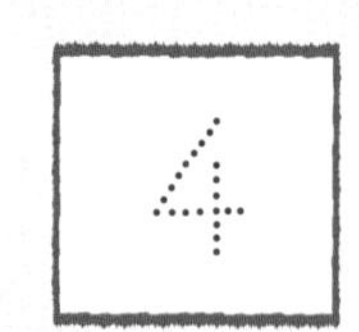

o'clock

Tell the time.
Write the numbers.

Activity

3 Play the game.

Let's begin!
I have 7 o'clock.
Who has 11 o'clock?

I have 11 o'clock.
Who has 8 o'clock?

I have 8 o'clock.
Who has 3 o'clock?

Activity

Match.

- April
- December
- January
- July
- November
- October

Activity

5 Look up the calendar.

Note: Help students to look up the dates in the month of April on a large wall calendar of the current year.

What day is it?
Match.

- Monday
- Tuesday
- Wednesday
- Thursday
- Friday
- Saturday
- Sunday

Activity

1 Play Snakes and Ladders!

Climb the ladder!
Show the correct number at each end of the ladder.

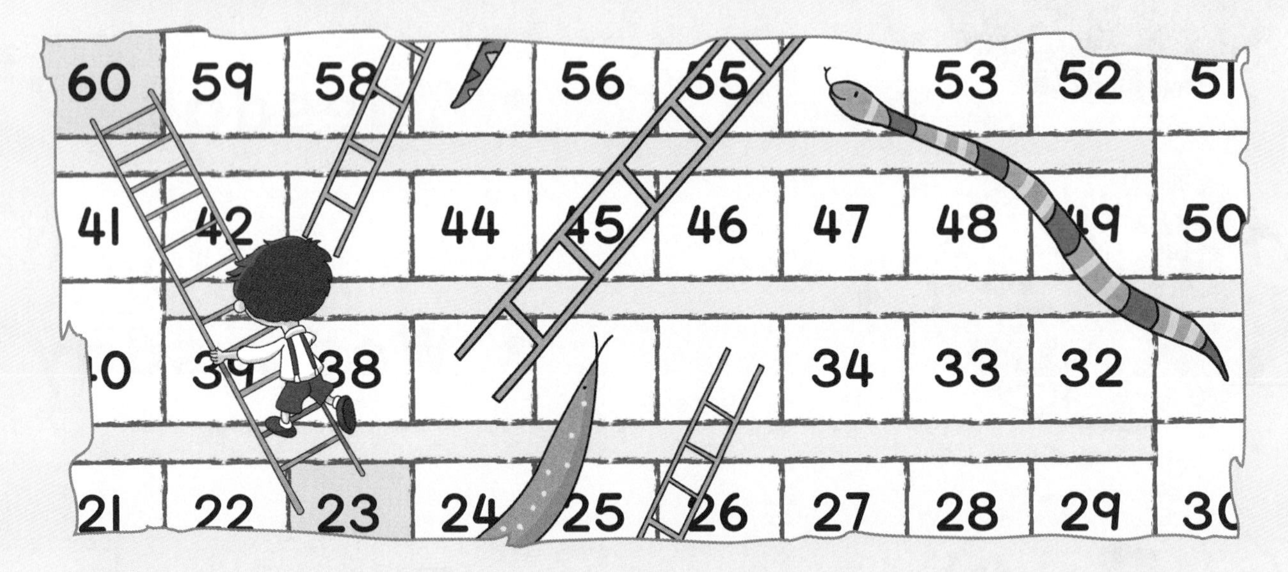

Make your friend slide down the snake!
Show the correct numbers at its head and tail.

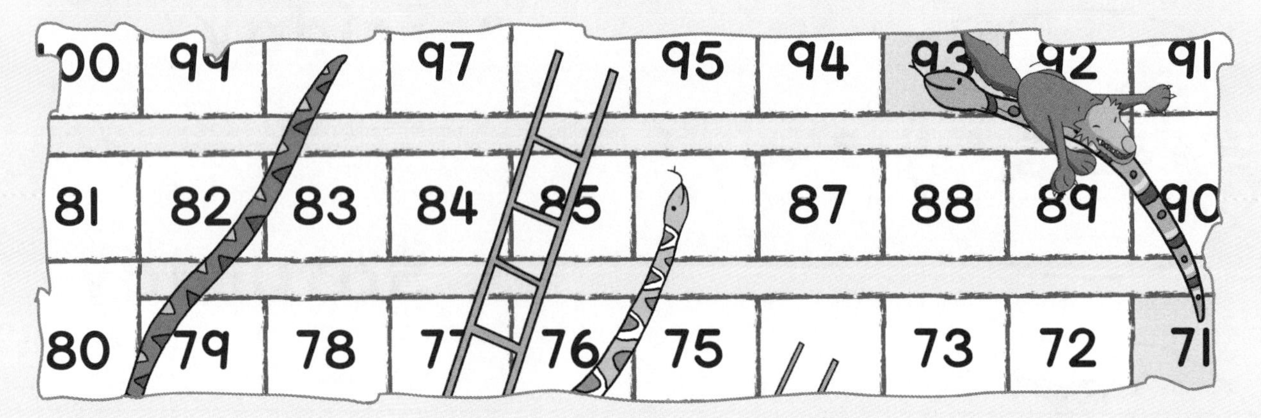

Note: To climb up the ladder or make their friend slide down the snake, students have to show the numbers at both ends of the ladder or snake respectively using the cutouts provided on page 139. Allow them to show consecutive numbers, e.g. they can show the numbers 60 and 61 in showing the number at the tail end of the orange snake connecting the 61 and 98 number squares.

Show the correct numbers.

100	99		97		95	94		92	91
81	82	83	84	85		87	88	89	90
80	79	78	77	76	75		73	72	
	62	63	64	65	66	67		69	70
	59	58		56	55		53	52	51
41	42		44	45	46	47	48	49	50
40	39	38				34	33	32	
21	22		24	25	26	27	28	29	30
20		18	17	16	15		13		11
1	2	3	4		6	7	8		10

Activity 2

Toss the dice.
Write the numbers.

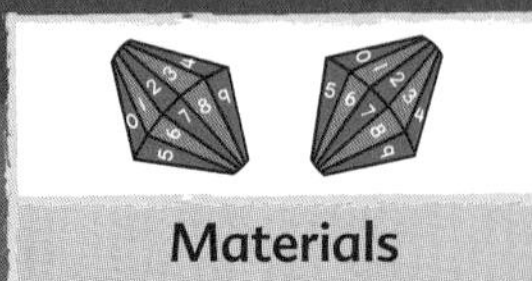

Note: In this activity, students toss two ten-sided dice to form a number with the numbers rolled and record it on the game board on the facing page. In the example illustrated, the girl formed the number 71 as the number 17 is on the board.

91	92	93	94				98		100
			84			87		89	
	72		74		76		78		80
61	62					67	68	69	
	52	53	54		56		58		60
41		43		45		47		49	
	32	33					38		
21		23	24	25		27		29	30
11	12			15		17			20
1	2	3	4	5	6	7	8	9	10

Activity

3

Cutouts: Pages 139 and 141

Paste the cutouts.
Count the flasks. Write the numbers.

Activity

Paste the cutouts.
Count the sheep. Write the numbers.

Activity

5 Count. Cry 'Wolf!'

5, 10, 15, 20,
25, 30, 35, 40 ...

Don't say '3'!
Cry 'Wolf!'

Say '5, 10, 15, 20, 25,
Wolf! Wolf! 40 ...'

Note: Students are to draw two cards, one from the sheep stack and another from the wolf stack from the cutouts on pages 143 and 145. In the example illustrated above, the boy picks the 'Count by 5's' sheep card and the '3' wolf card. He has to count in 5's and replace any number with the digit '3' by crying, "Wolf!" Guide students to count by counting the squares on the 1 to 100 chart provided.

Use the 1 to 100 chart.

91	92	93	94	95	96	97	98	99	100
81	82	83	84	85	86	87	88	89	90
71	72	73	74	75	76	77	78	79	80
61	62	63	64	65	66	67	68	69	70
51	52	53	54	55	56	57	58	59	60
41	42	43	44	45	46	47	48	49	50
31	32	33	34	35	36	37	38	39	40
21	22	23	24	25	26	27	28	29	30
11	12	13	14	15	16	17	18	19	20
1	2	3	4	5	6	7	8	9	10

How much does each toy cost? Write the amount.

cents

cents

cents

Activity
2
Pay for the things. Paste the cutouts.

Cutouts: Pages 147 and 149

Activity

3

Pay for the things.
Paste the cutouts.

Cutouts: Pages 149 and 151

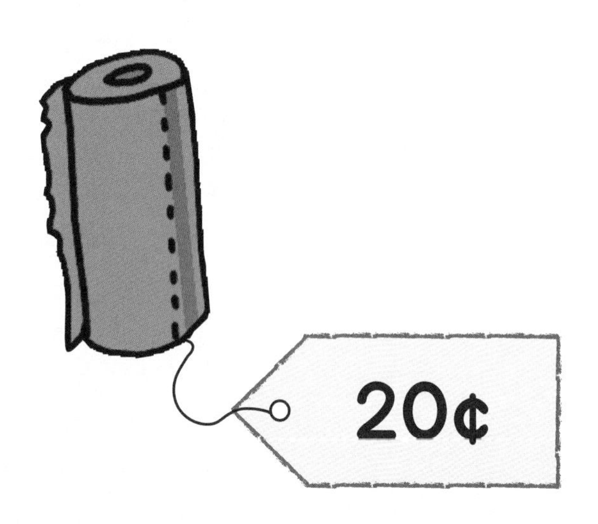

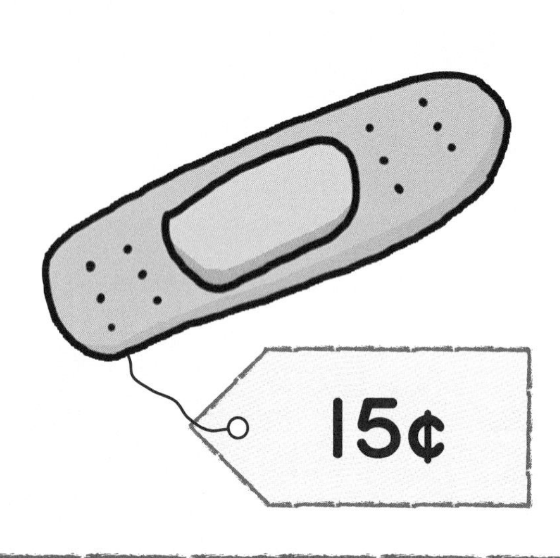

Pay for the things.
Paste the cutouts.

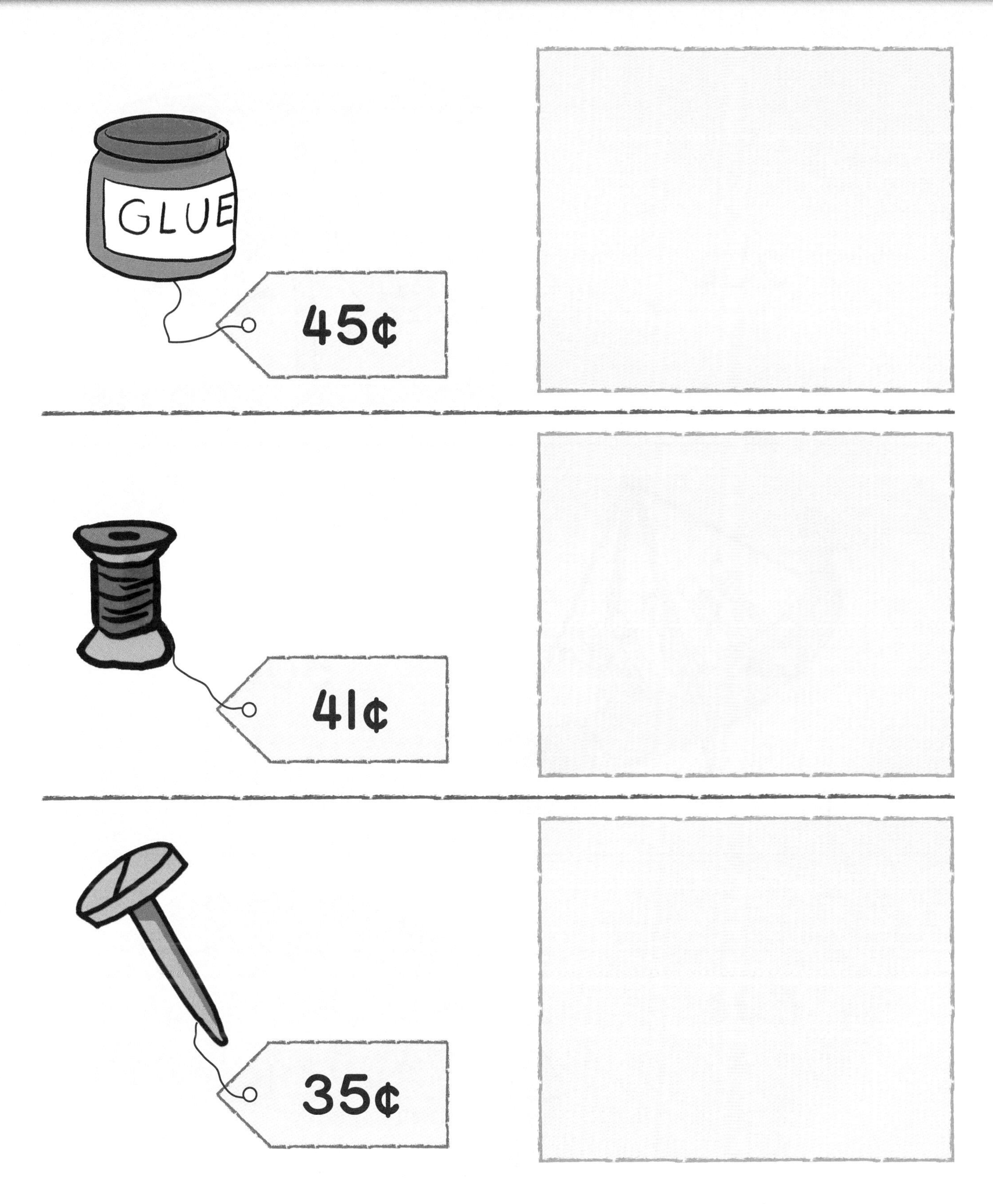

Activity

4 Pay for the rides.

Cutouts: Page 153

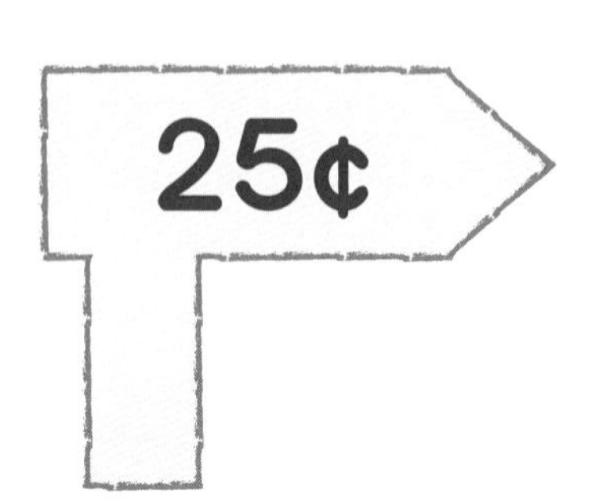

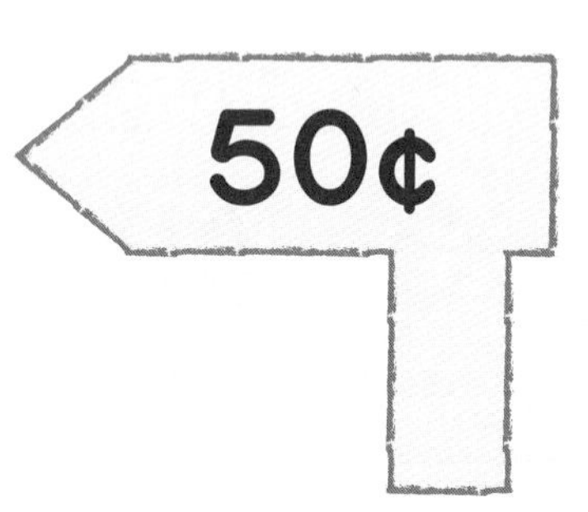

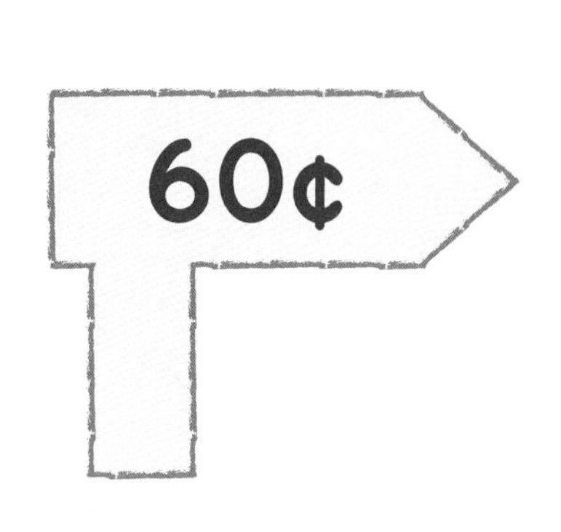

Pay for the rides.

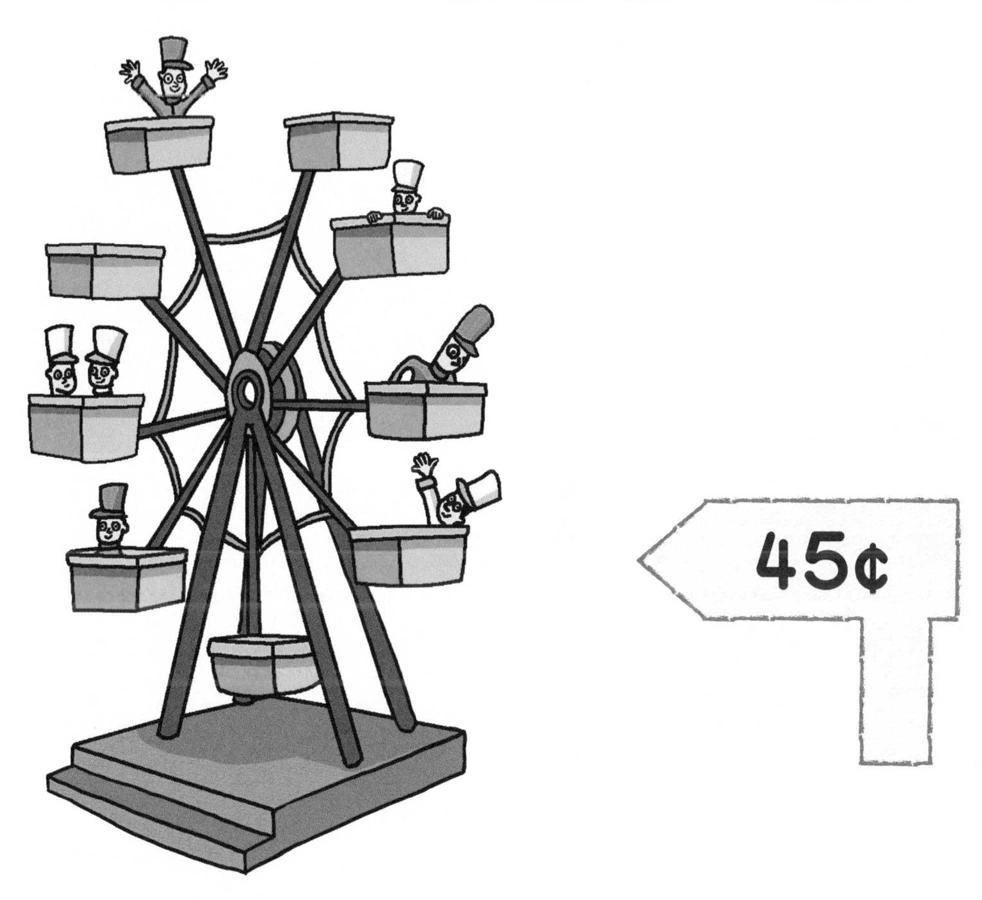

Activity
5 How much money is there? Paste the cutouts.

Cutouts: Page 155

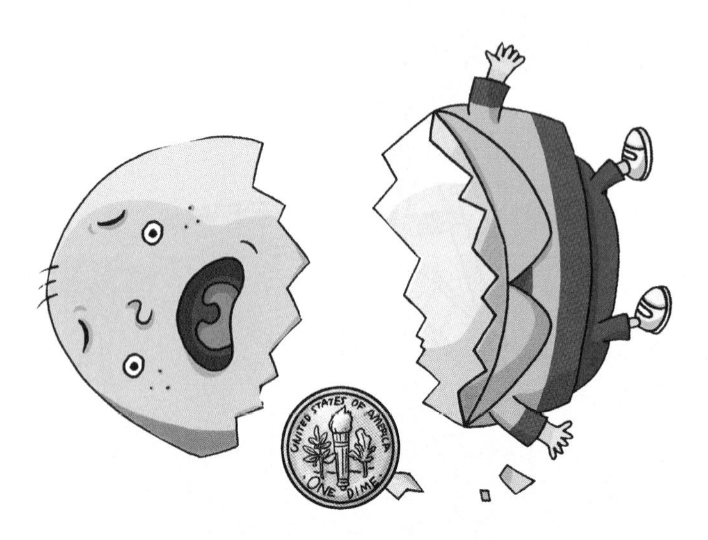

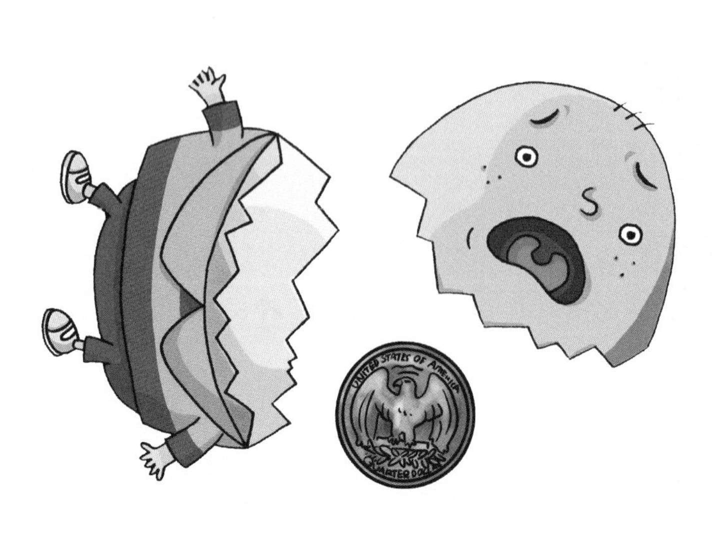

How much money is there?
Paste the cutouts.

Blank

Cutouts for pages 18 and 19

0	1	2	3	4	5	6
7	8	9	10	11	12	13
14	15	16	17	18	19	20
10	10	10	10	10	10	10
10	10	10				

Cutouts for pages 20 and 21

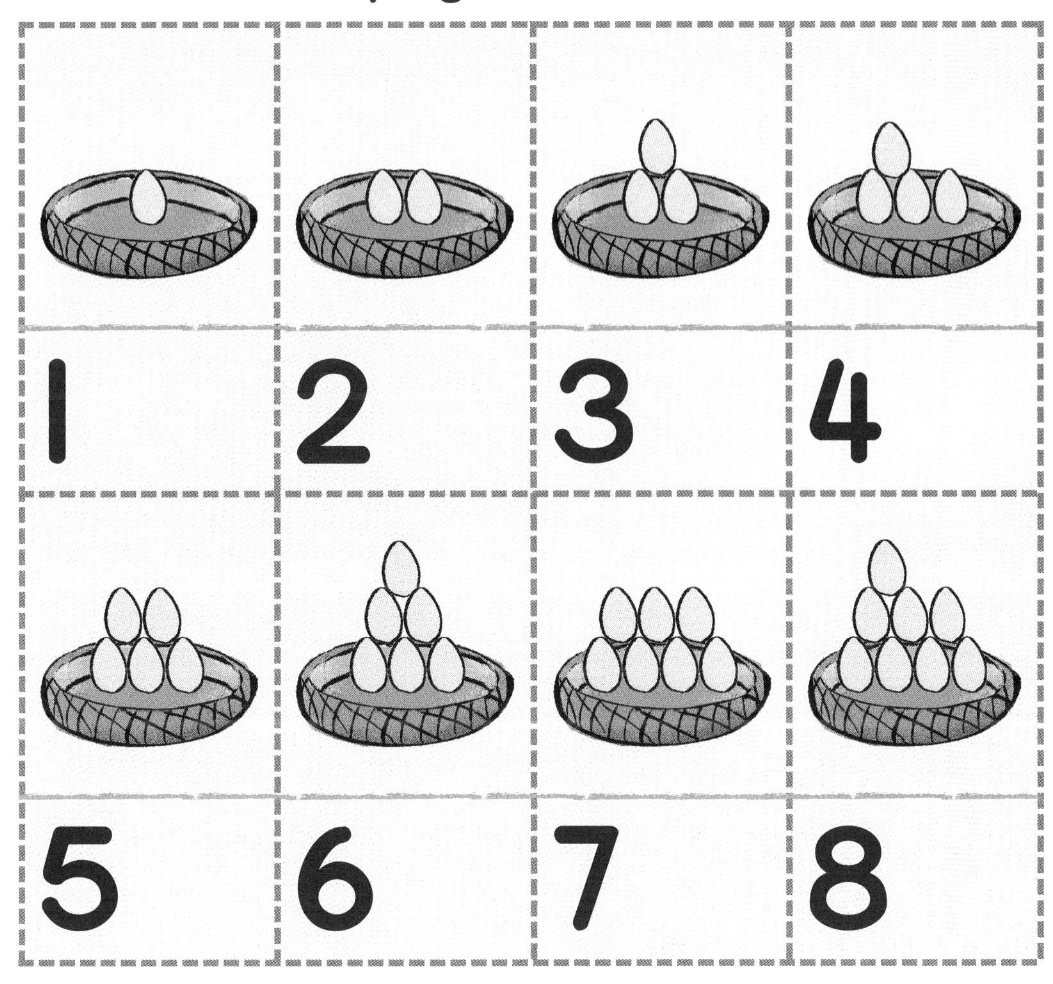

Cutouts for pages 20 and 21 (continued)

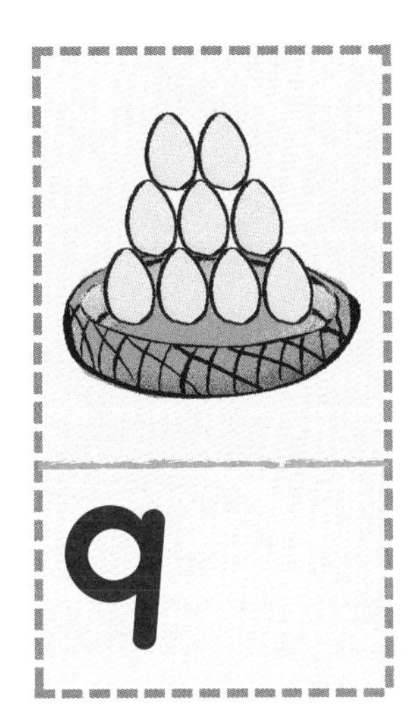

Cutouts for pages 25 and 26

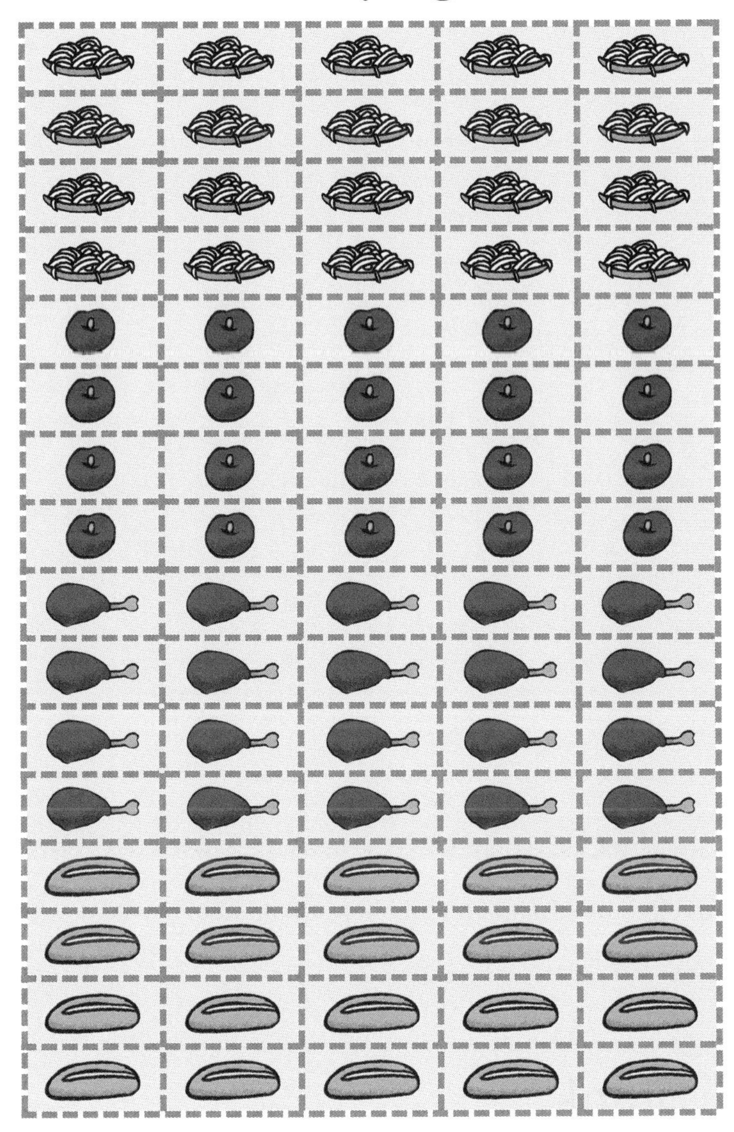

Blank

Cutouts for page 27

1	2	3
4	5	6
7	8	9
10	11	12

Blank

Cutouts for page 27 (continued)

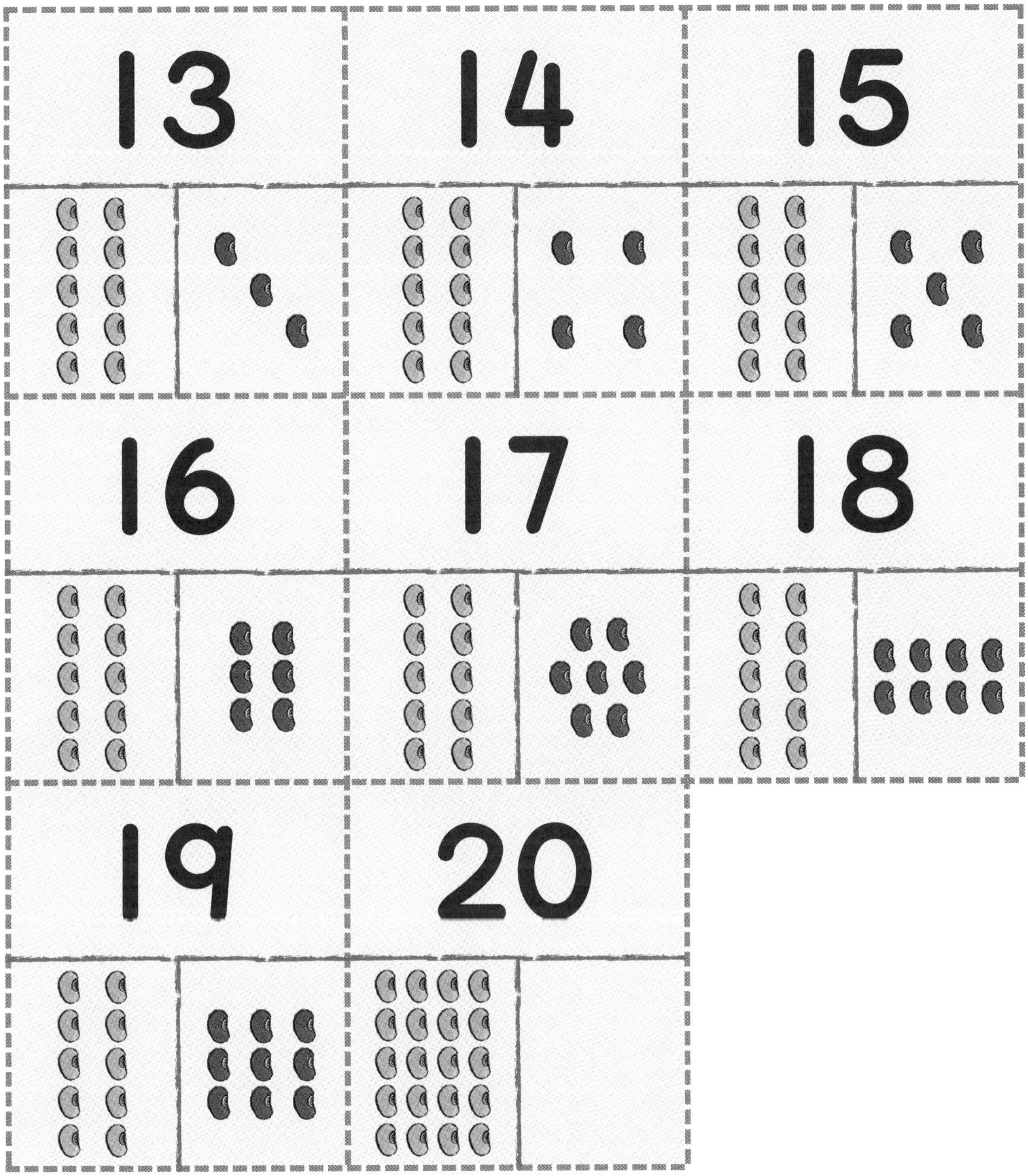

13	14	15
16	17	18
19	20	

Cutouts for pages 28 to 30

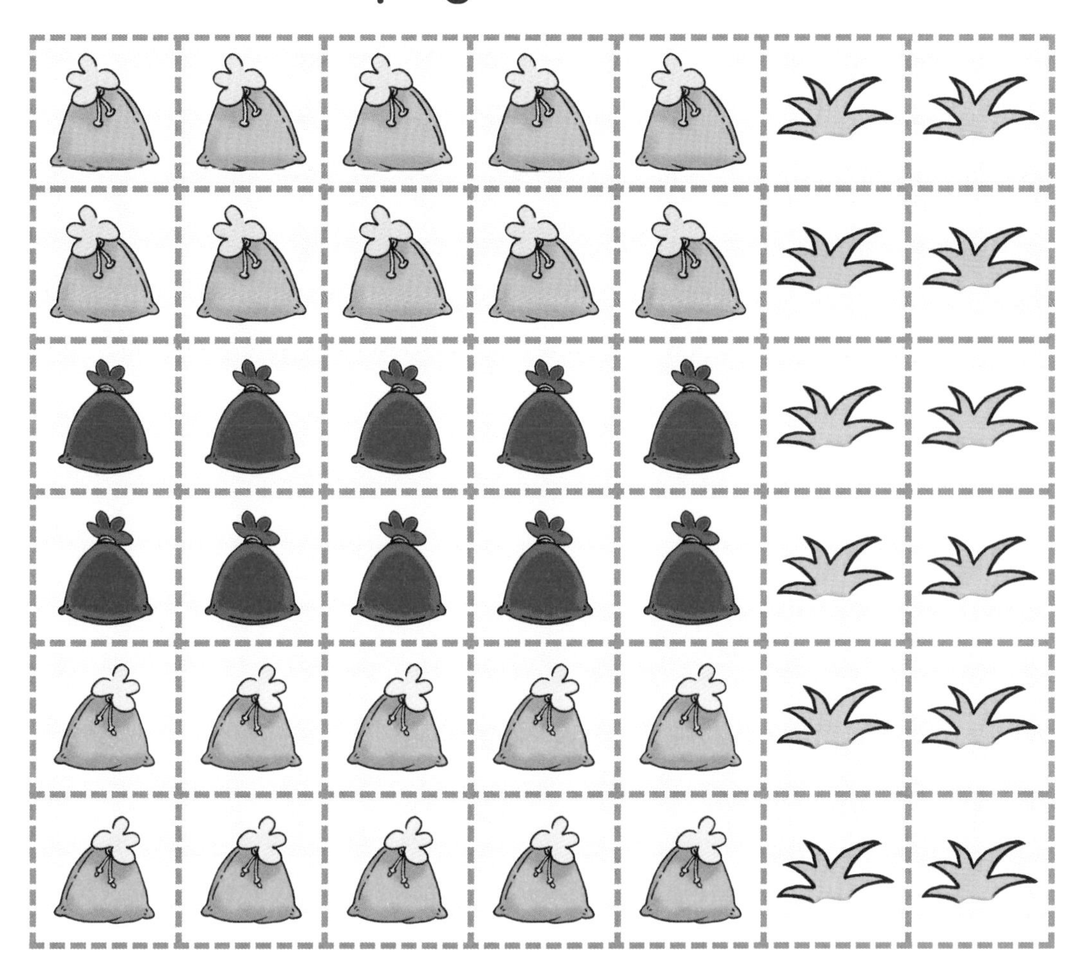

Cutouts for page 37

Blank

Cutouts for pages 38 and 39

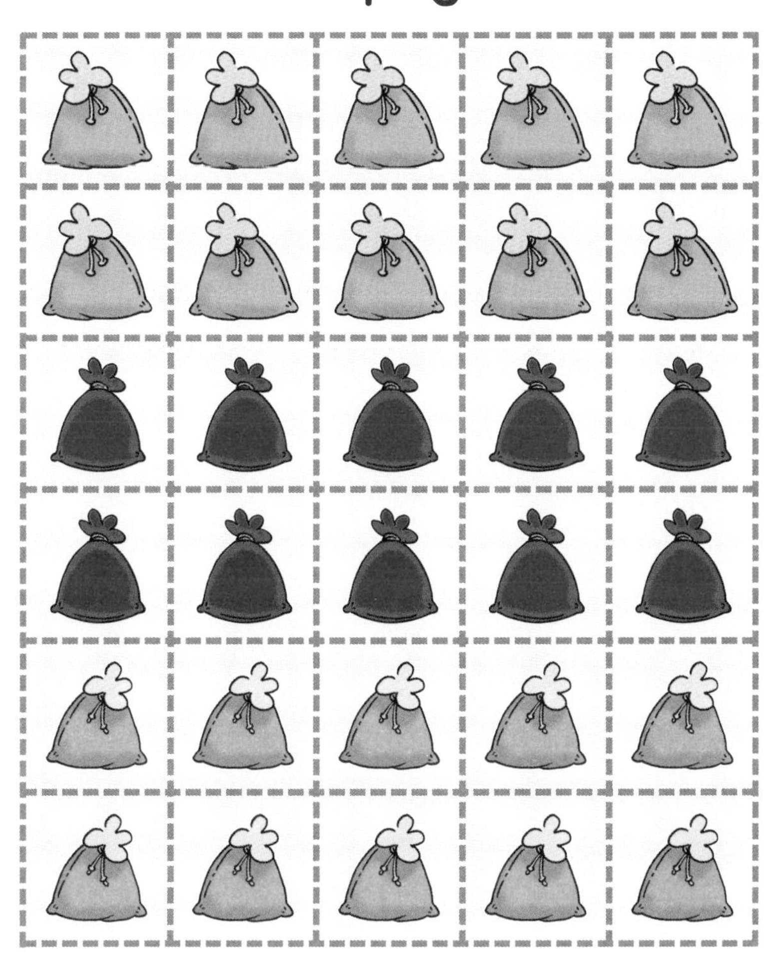

Cutouts for pages 45 to 47

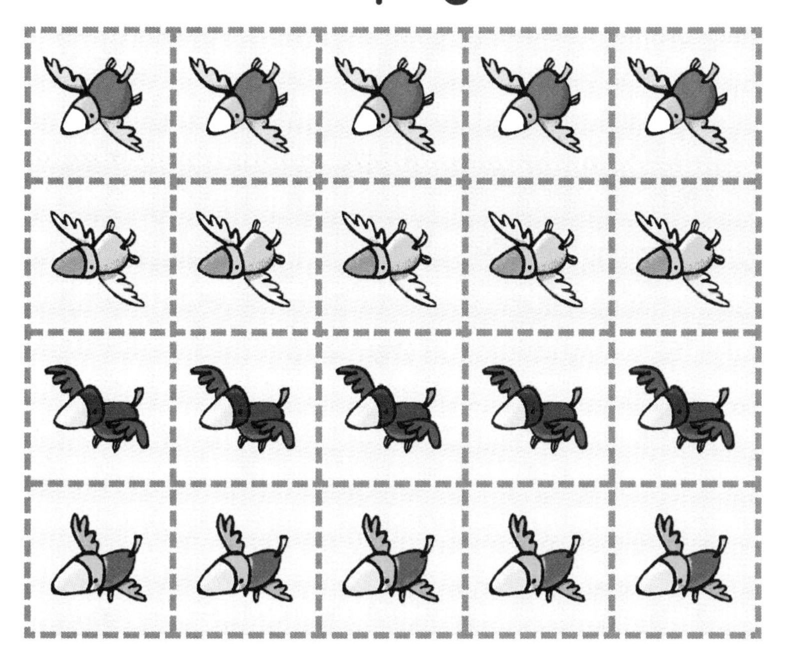

Cutouts for pages 52 and 53

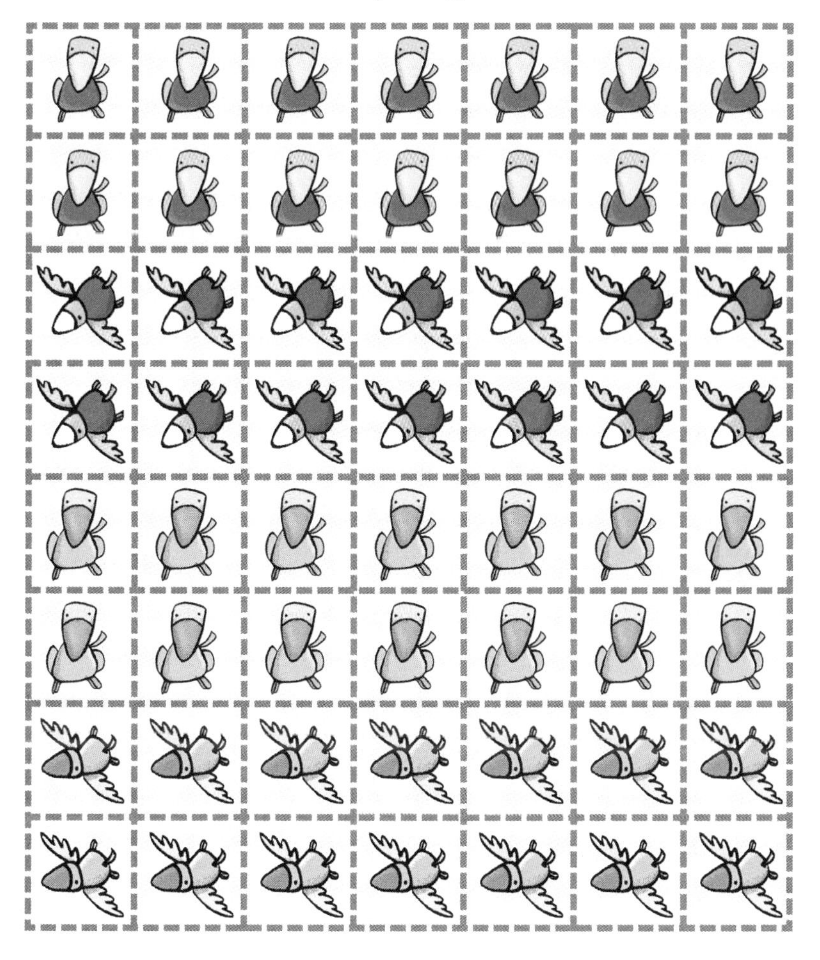

Blank

Cutouts for pages 54 to 61

Blank

Cutouts for pages 64 and 65

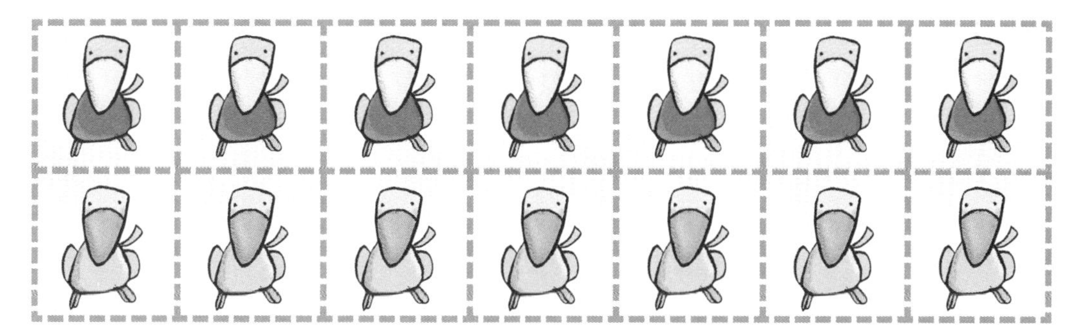

Cutouts for pages 66 and 67

Cutouts for pages 68 and 69

Blank

Cutouts for page 70

1 2 3

4 4 5

5 6 7

8 9 10

Cutouts for pages 71 and 72

0	1	2	3	4	5	6
7	8	9	10	21	22	23
24	25	26	27	28	29	30
20	20	20	20	20	20	20
20	20	20				

Cutouts for pages 73 and 74

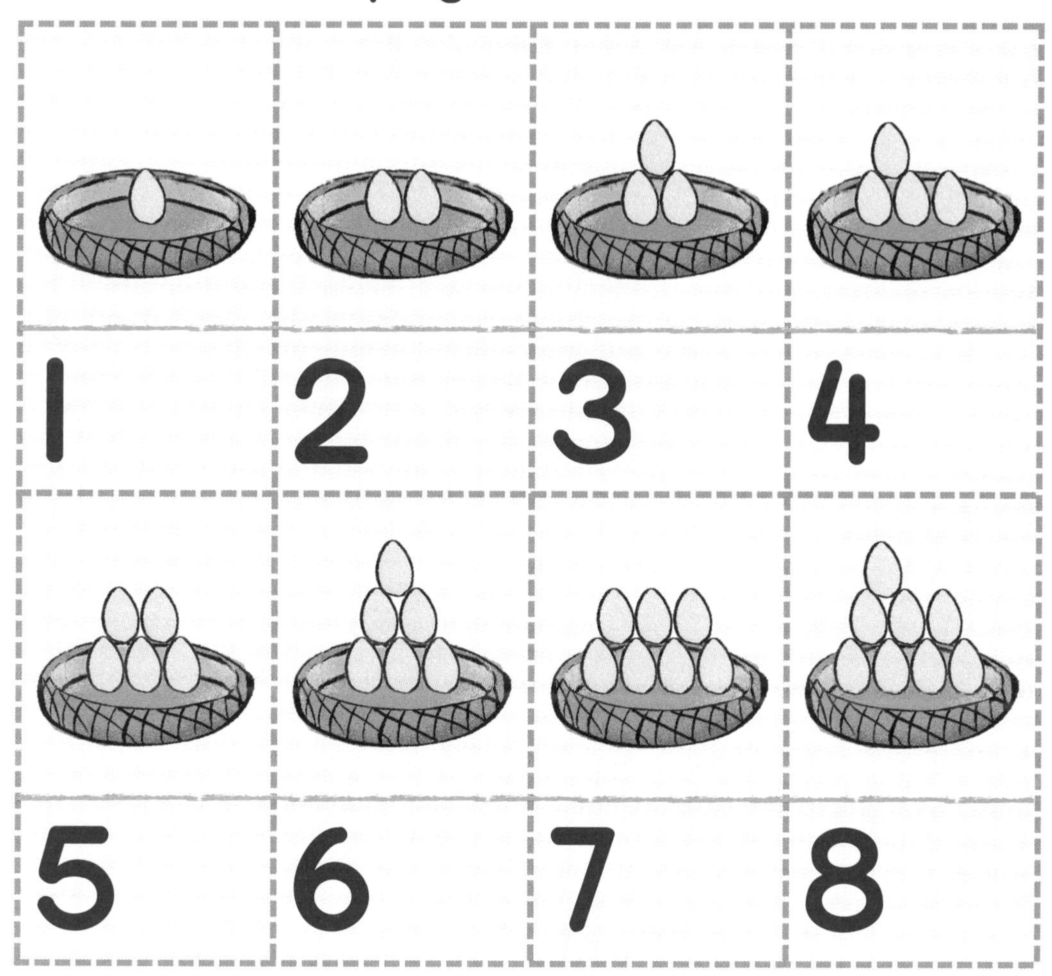

Blank

Cutouts for pages 73 and 74 (continued)

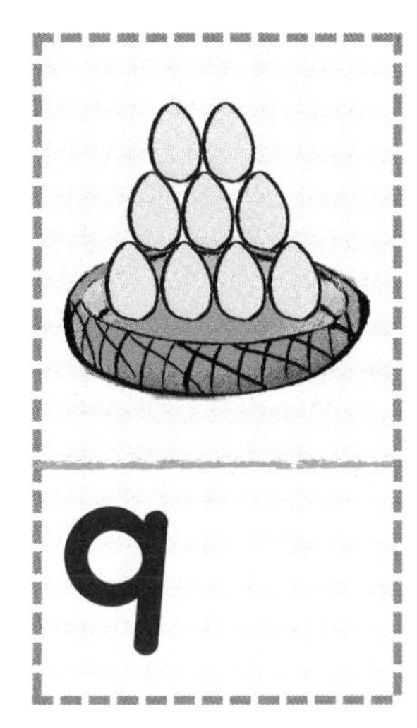

Cutouts for page 75

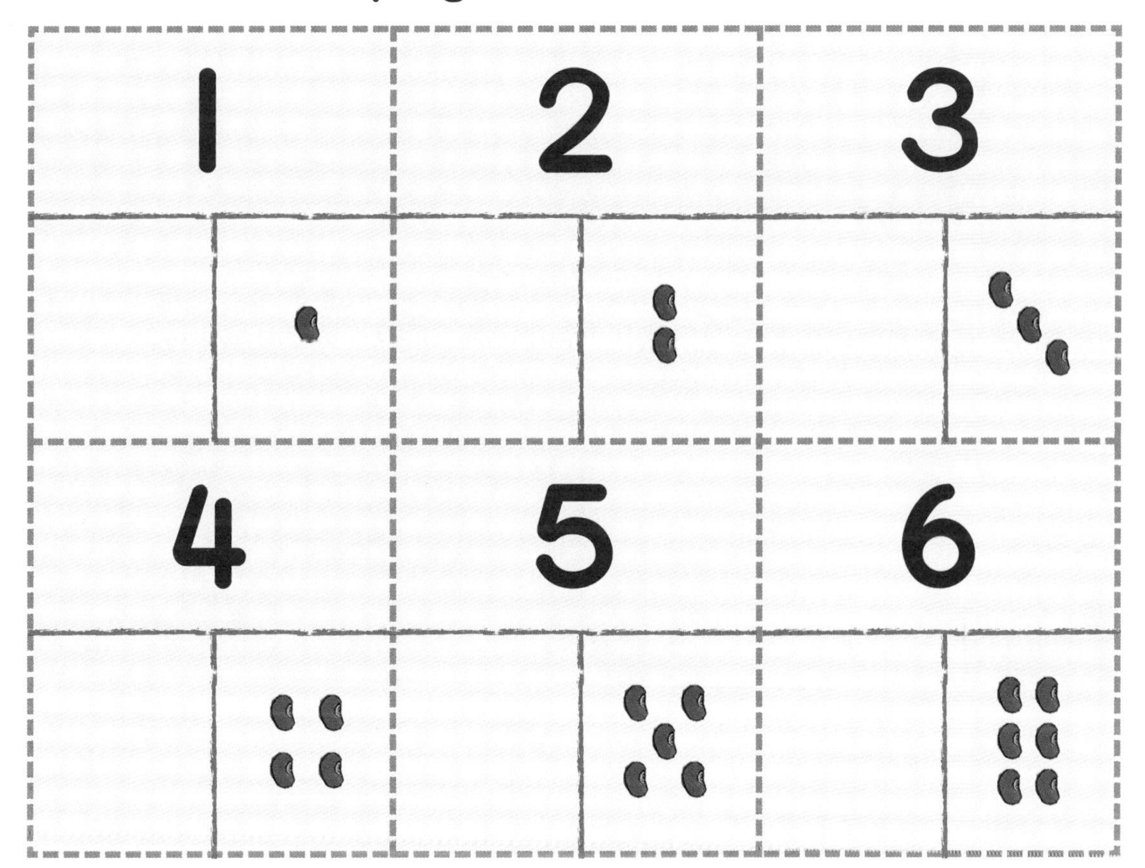

Cutouts for page 75 (continued)

7		8		9	

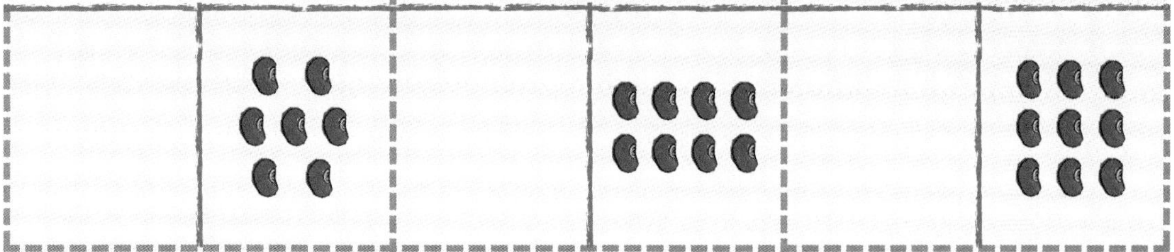

10		11		12	

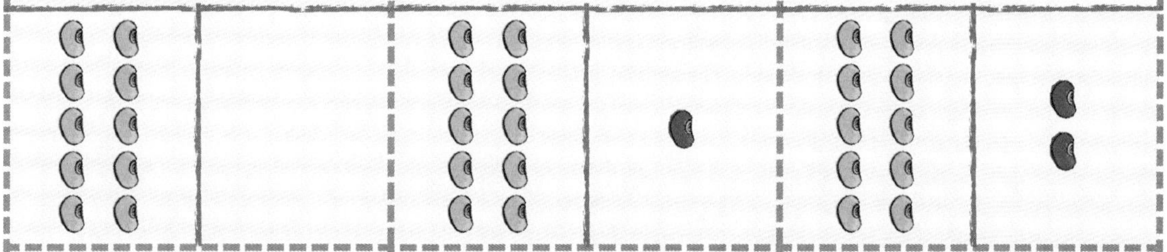

13		14		15	

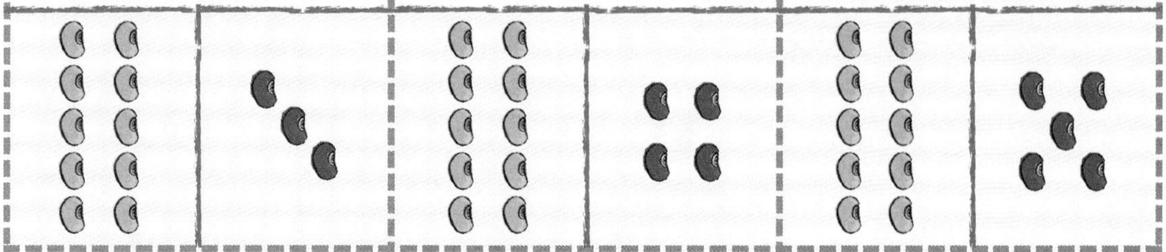

16		17		18	

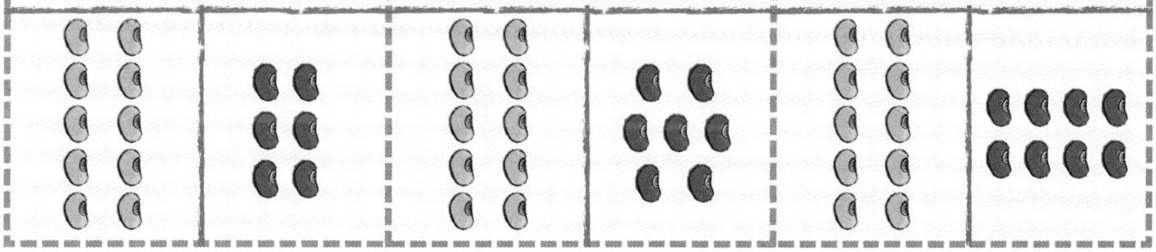

Blank

Cutouts for page 75 (continued)

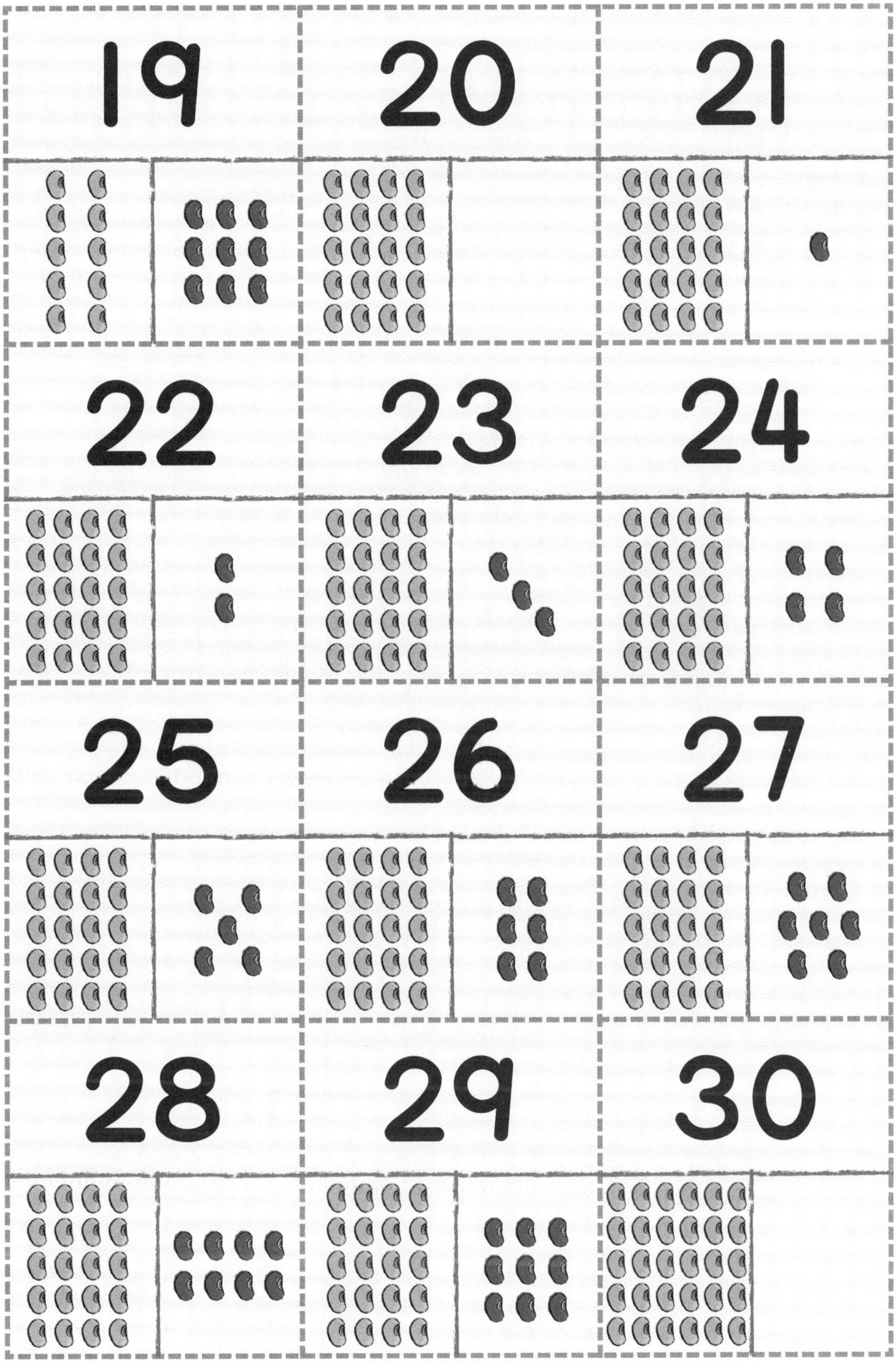

19	20	21
22	23	24
25	26	27
28	29	30

Cutouts for pages 76 and 77

1	2	3	4
5	6	7	8
9	10	11	12
13	14	15	16
17	18	19	20
21	22	23	24
25	26	27	28
29	30		

Cutouts for pages 78 and 79

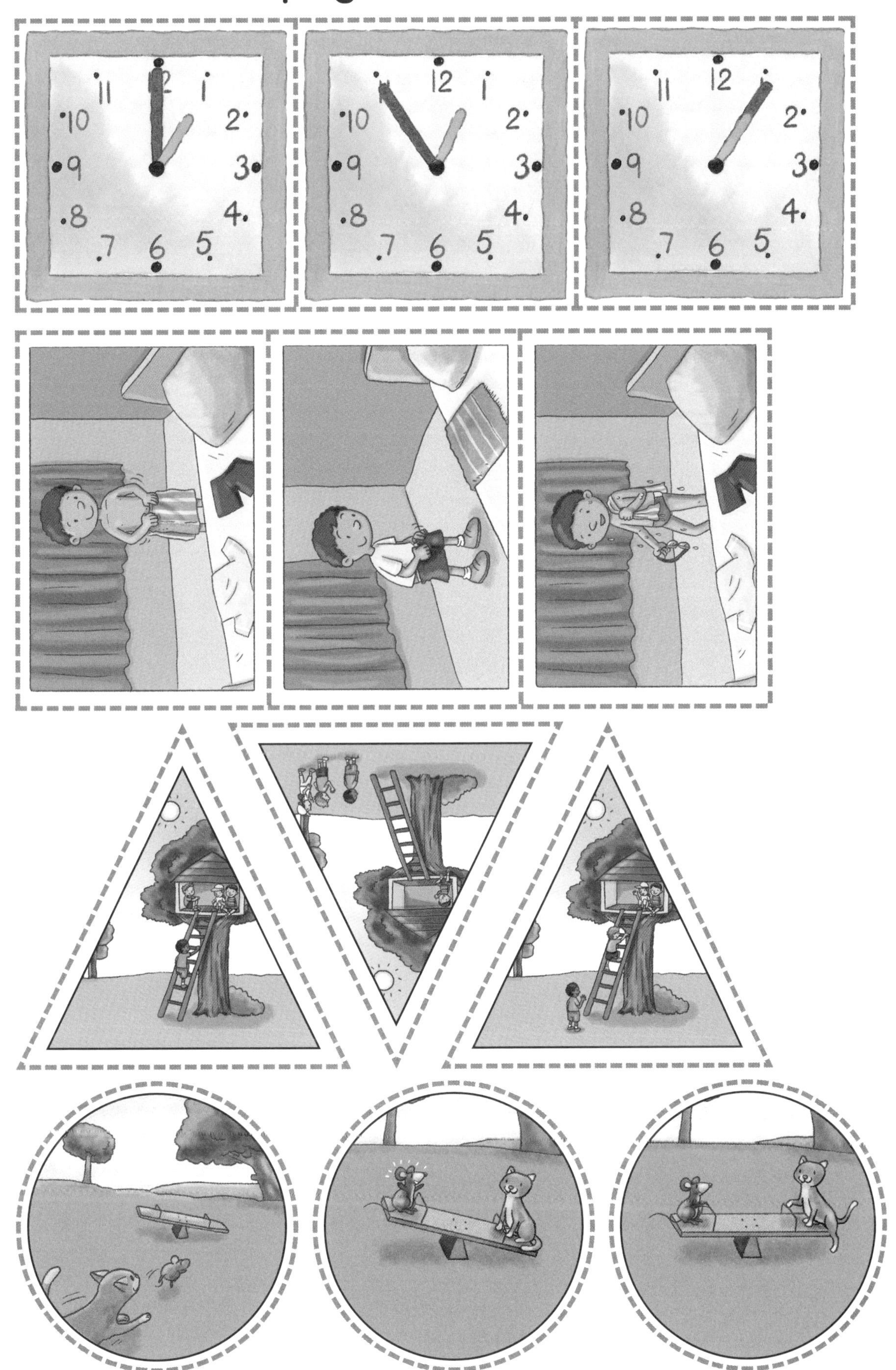

Cutouts for page 82

I have  • Who has  ?

I have  • Who has  ?

I have  • Who has  ?

I have  • Who has  ?

I have  • Who has  ?

I have  • Who has  ?

Blank

Cutouts for page 82 (continued)

I have  • Who has  ?

I have  • Who has  ?

I have  • Who has  ?

I have  • Who has  ?

I have  • Who has  ?

I have  • Who has  ?

Blank

Cutouts for pages 86 and 87

10	20	30	40	50	60	70	80	90	100
9	19	29	39	49	59	69	79	89	99
8	18	28	38	48	58	68	78	88	98
7	17	27	37	47	57	67	77	87	97
6	16	26	36	46	56	66	76	86	96
5	15	25	35	45	55	65	75	85	95
4	14	24	34	44	54	64	74	84	94
3	13	23	33	43	53	63	73	83	93
2	12	22	32	42	52	62	72	82	92
1	11	21	31	41	51	61	71	81	91

Cutouts for page 90

Blank

Cutouts for page 90 (continued)

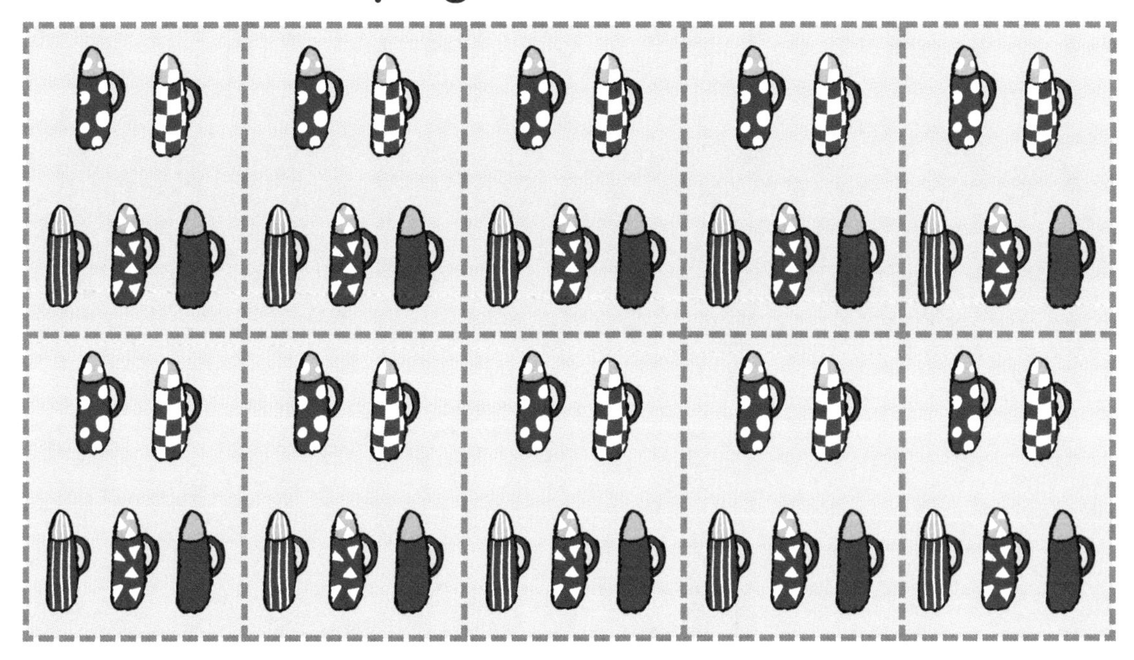

Cutouts for page 91

Blank

Cutouts for pages 92 and 93

Cutouts for pages 92 and 93 (continued)

Cutouts for page 95

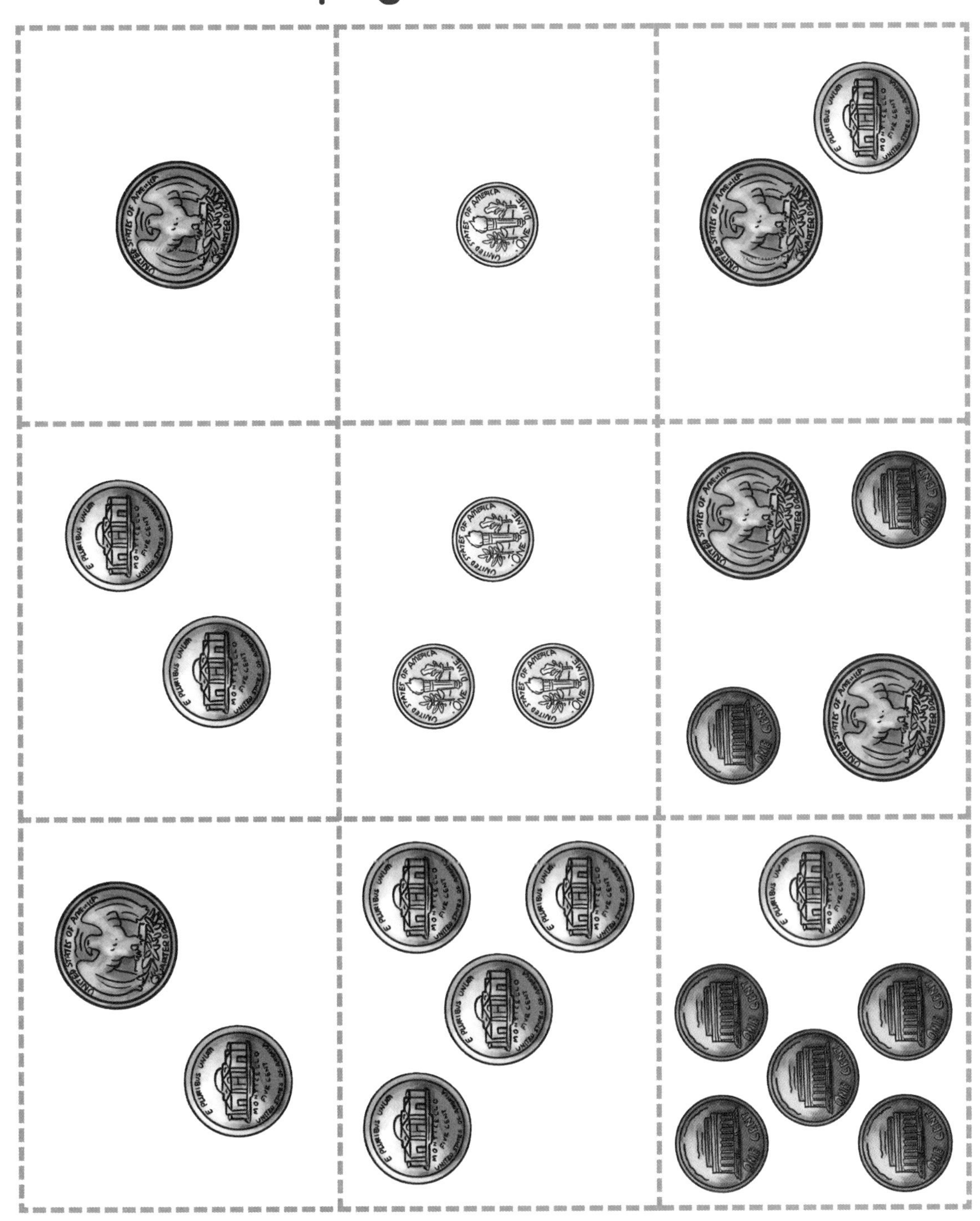

Blank

Cutouts for page 95 (continued)

Cutouts for pages 96 and 97

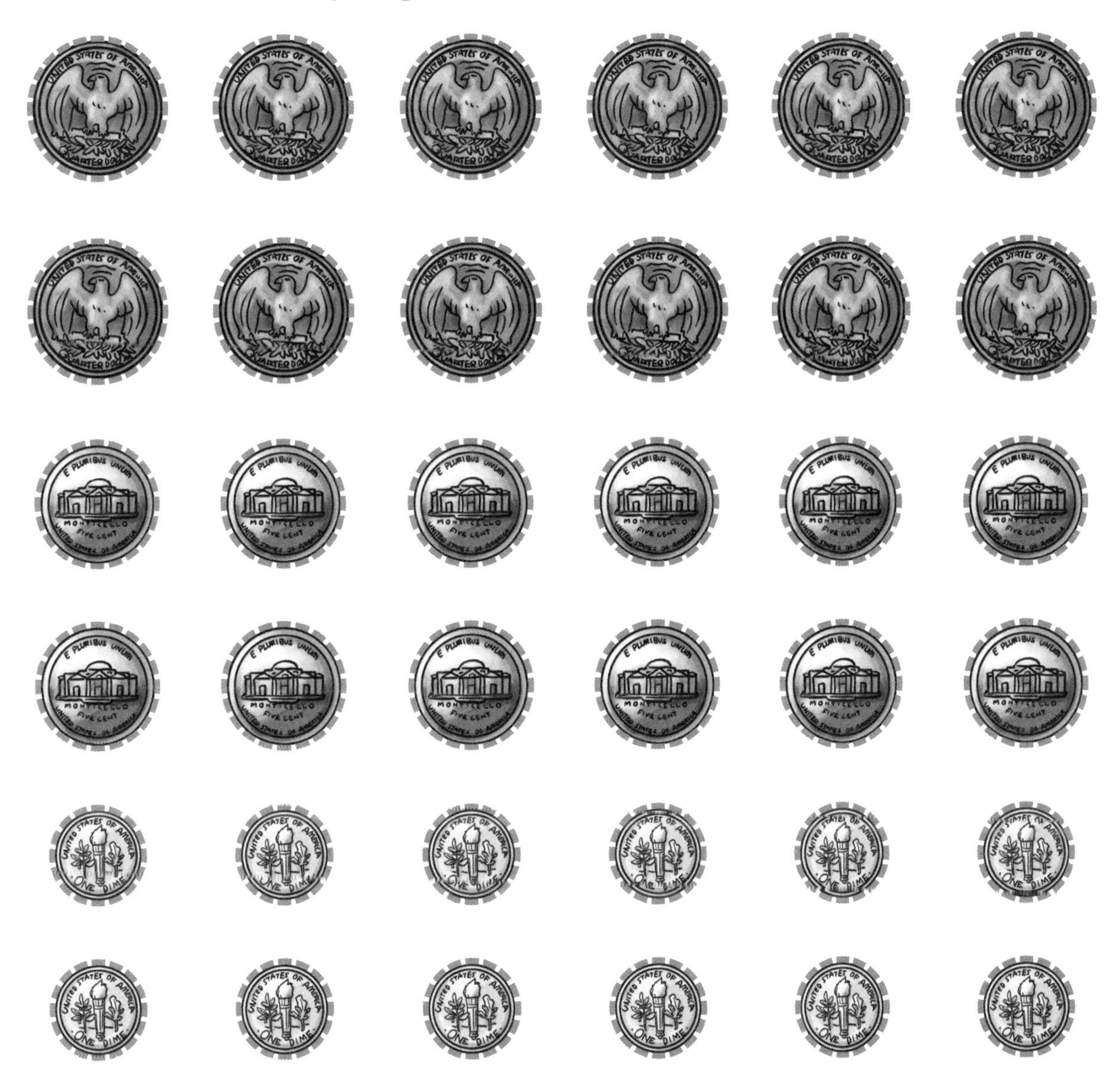

Cutouts for pages 96 and 97 (continued)

Cutouts for pages 98 and 99

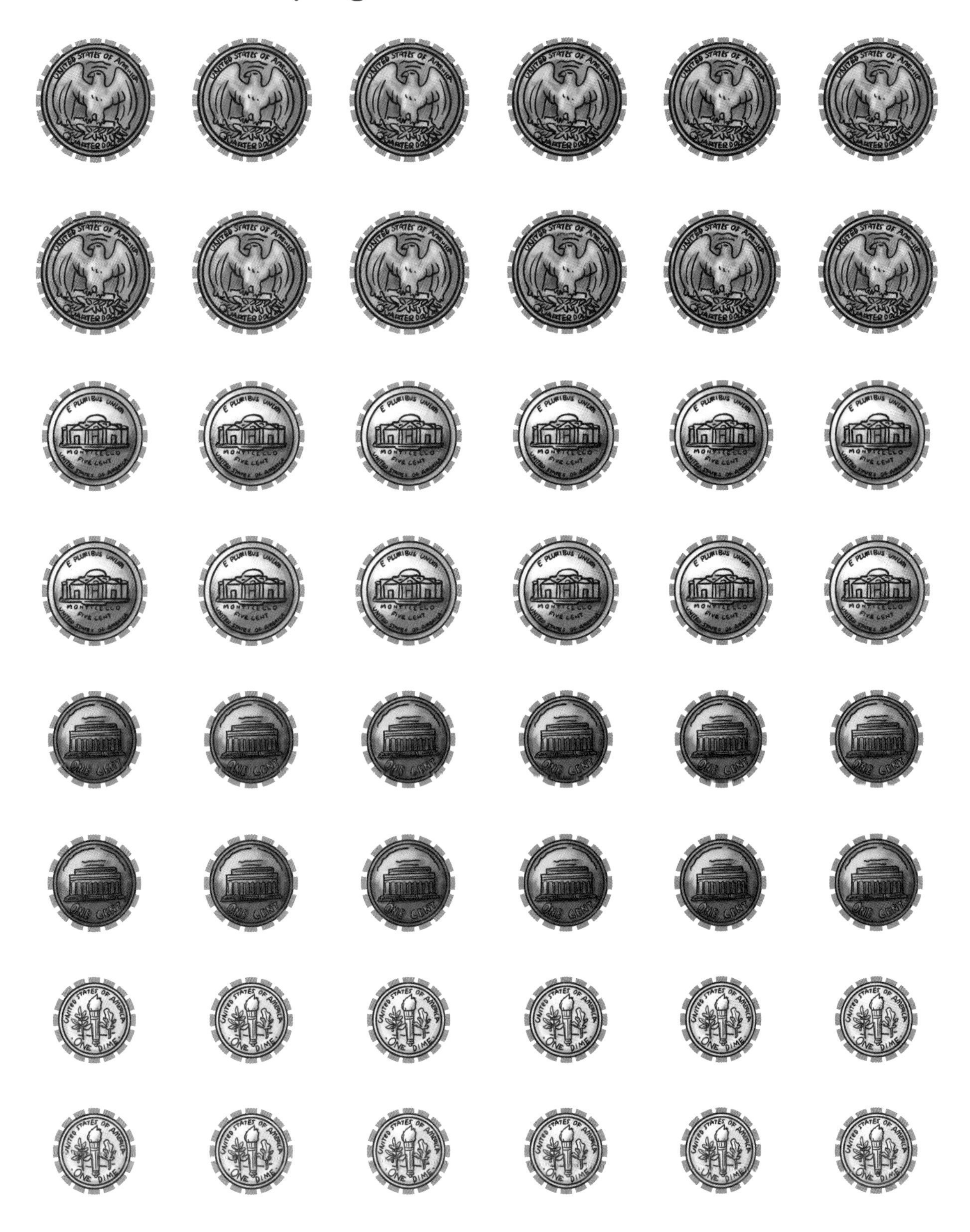

Blank

Cutouts for pages 100 and 101

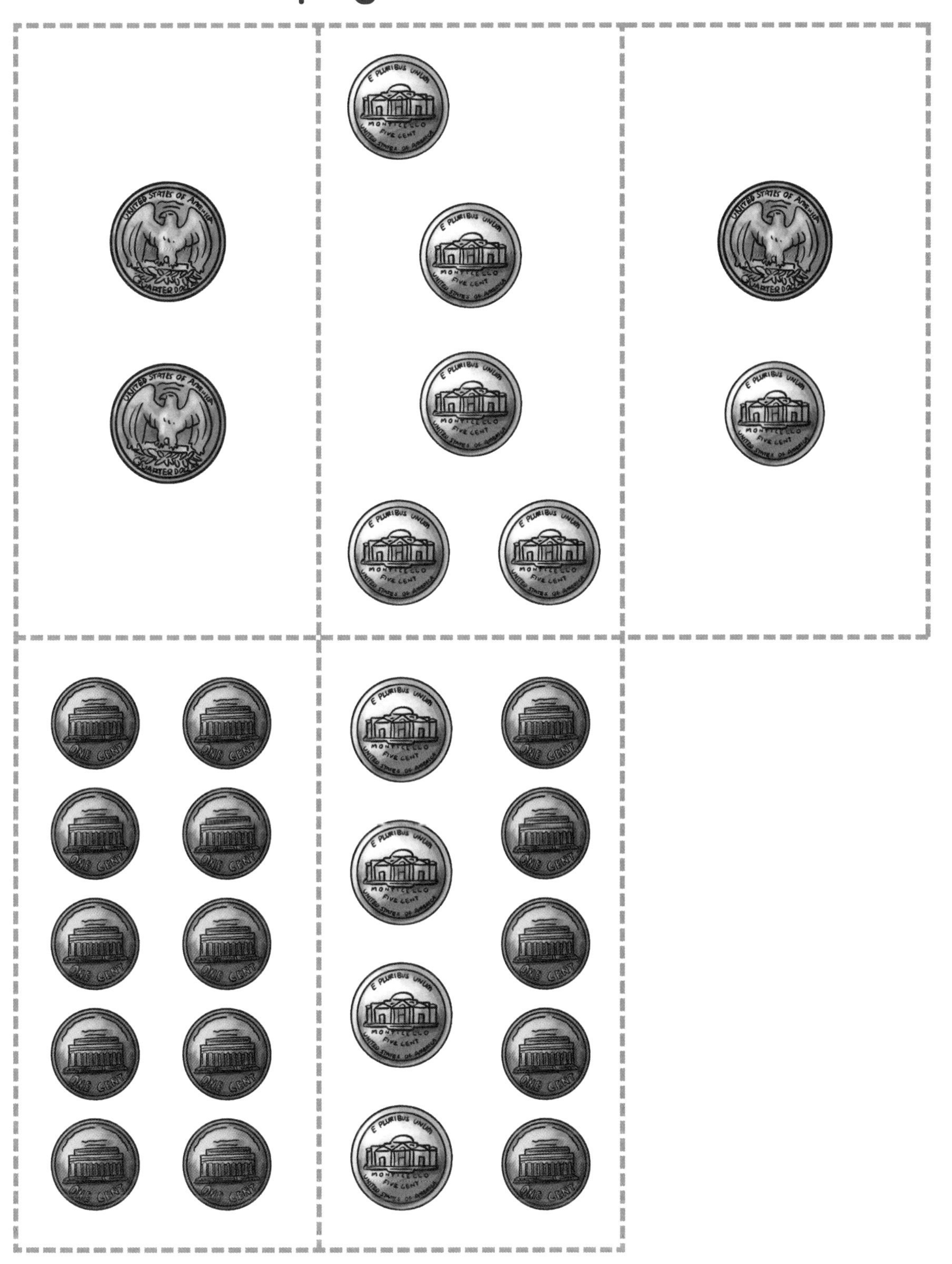

Blank